Mastering Old Testament Facts

| PROGRAMMED READING |
| ART AND ACTIVITIES |
| TESTS |

to get it all down PAT

BOOK 1
Introduction and Pentateuch

Madeline H. Beck
Lamar Williamson, Jr.

Sketches
MARTHA WILLIAMSON

John Knox Press
ATLANTA

International Standard Book Number: 0-8042-0134-X
© John Knox Press 1978
Printed in the United States of America

PREFACE

The Old Testament

The book you are about to read is Sacred Scripture for three of the world's great religions. It is <u>the</u> Scripture for Judaism. Islam, while giving highest authority to the Koran, still understands Israel's Scripture to be inspired and holy. Christians call these books the "Old Testament." They comprise about three-fourths of the Christian Bible, while writings of the early Church, called the "New Testament," make up one-fourth. When the New Testament writers speak of the "Scriptures," it is almost always to the Old Testament that they refer.

Men and women of all three faiths, as well as those of other faiths and those of no faith, continue to find the books of the Old Testament appealing, nourishing, beautiful, and stimulating -- as well as annoying, boring and difficult. Many believe that these writings come from God; all agree that they belong to all humankind. None who care about humanity or literature or God should try to live in ignorance of their content.

This Book

Mastering Old Testament Facts is a guide for individuals or groups who want to know the basic content of the Old Testament. While it has been designed for individual use, it can easily be adapted for use by study groups or classes.

Like its companion, *Mastering New Testament Facts,* it can be used in local churches and military chapels, as a course supplement in schools and colleges, by candidates preparing for ordination exams, by potential church officers or teachers, and by individuals at home.

Purpose and Stance

The purpose of *Mastering Old Testament Facts* is in one way very modest. It focuses on a limited selection of basic content items: outline and sequence, persons, places, events, and characteristic features. Historical, literary, and theological questions are set aside or receive only minimal attention.

In another sense, however, the purpose of this book is quite ambitious. The user should achieve 90 percent mastery of the material taught, or 70 percent growth above low pre-test scores.

By "facts" the authors intend no historical judgment. In line with it's purpose, this guide aims at neutrality on debated historical and theological issues. Though it is impossible to read or to ask questions about a text without some interpretation, the authors have made a conscious effort to reduce interpretive elements to a minimum and to leave the users maximum room for discussion and private judgment.

Suggestions for Individual Study

1. Read and follow carefully each set of instructions, beginning with "Before You Use This Book," page 1.

2. Plan for sufficient time at each sitting to finish a logical block of biblical material, but not so long as to get bored or tired (30 minutes to 2 hours).

3. The Good News Bible (Today's English Version) is the most helpful translation to use with *Mastering Old Testament Facts*. However, other versions of the Old Testament may be used if differences in wording do not upset you.

4. Given the limited purpose of this book, you may wish to supplement it with a good commentary, Bible dictionary and atlas.

Suggestions for Group Study

1. Each participant should have a copy of *Mastering Old Testament Facts* and the Good News Bible.

2. The leader should help participants with instructions in the book that might not be clear to some.

3. The group should balance time for discussion with time for individual study. Either covenant to spend an agreed time in individual study outside class, or use alternate meeting periods for individual study and for group discussion, or use half of each class period for individual work and the remaining half for discussion.

4. During individual study each participant should note one or two points most urgently needing group attention.

5. Someone should be responsible to look for other resources when group discussion does not resolve difficulties.

6. The leader should be sure all members have opportunites to participate, and that there is both freedom and direction in the discussion.

CONTENTS

BEFORE YOU USE THIS BOOK . . .

This study guide to the Old Testament appears in four books and has been designed to help you learn the content and structure of the Old Testament in the shortest possible time.

The books are:
1. *Introduction and Pentateuch*
2. *Historical Books*
3. *Poetry and Wisdom*
4. *Prophetic Writings*

Description

All four books use the PAT system (Programmed reading, Art and activities, and Tests), which enables the student to get the facts down pat. The approach followed is one which uses learning methods successfully employed both in public school education and in industry, but adapted to the biblical material. *Mastering Old Testament Facts* incorporates some aspects of programmed instruction and some aspects of a workbook. All of the techniques used in this study -- pre-tests, guided reading, drawings, charts, section and unit tests --are ways of preparing or reinforcing one's memory. The goal is 90 percent mastery of the items selected for retention, or 70 percent growth.

Learning Process

Mastery of this material proceeds through five stages -- one diagnostic, and four learning and evaluative.

1. Pre-test

The first diagnostic stage is the pre-test you will take before you begin each unit. It will measure your present mastery of the Bible content taught in that unit and will acquaint you with the types of questions you will be expected to answer. It is not an evaluation but a way of learning, so don't be disturbed if you do not know the material. If you already know it, you do not need to study it. On the other hand, the lower your pre-test score, the more gratifying may be your growth as measured by the final (unit) test.

2. Guided Reading

As you begin to learn, you will be asked to read the Bible itself a few chapters at a time. *Mastering Old Testament Facts* will guide you as you read by numbered outline headings which call attention to the structure of the biblical book and by questions which invite you to notice certain items in the passage. Guided reading pages are divided into three or four parts, each of which is called a "frame." You will not read straight down the page, but you will work through all the top frames of one unit before returning to begin working through the second frames on each page.

Both the numbers and the capitalization of the frame headings will help you remember the biblical book's outline if you use them properly. The first digit usually refers to the biblical book and the second digit (or last two, for complex outlines) refers to major divisions in the book, while capital letters at the end of a heading number refer to subdivisions. Do not be surprised if outline numbers jump from 12 to 20, for instance, as you move from First to Second Chronicles! Major divisions are written in ALL CAPITAL LETTERS and subheadings are Initially Capitalized.

<u>Drawings</u> on question pages are used to reinforce your learning of the book's structure. Drawings on answer pages will reinforce one or two of the items taught in each frame.

3. Section Tests

At the end of each biblical book, or on completion of an entire series of frames, you will be tested on items emphasized in the guided reading. You may refresh your memory of the structure, major themes and key quotations by studying the <u>chart</u> provided for each book just before you take the section test. Due to the large amount of significant items in some of the books (like Samuel and Kings), section tests will not always include every item to which your attention has been drawn. However, they will include every item you are expected to retain, organized into categories which will help you to know what you are learning and to measure your progress in each area. If you score less than 90 percent on any part of the section test, you should review the relevant material in the study guide and in the Old Testament.

4. Unit Test

When you have completed all sections at the 90 percent level, a final test will evaluate your mastery of the biblical books in each unit. By using the scoring charts and growth record at the back of the study guide you can easily determine your growth in knowledge of biblical content.

5. Study References

Scripture references are given for all <u>unit test</u> answers. By checking the references for any items you miss on a unit test, you can complete your mastery of this unit's content. If you score less than 90 percent you should review any areas of weakness before proceeding to another unit. This does not apply if your growth from the score you made on the pre-test was more than 70 percent.

A Warning and a Wish

You should be warned that even if you make 100 percent on all tests, it would not mean that you have mastered the Bible! Remember that these tests measure <u>knowledge of content</u> only. The vast history of Israel out of which the Old Testament sprang, its intricate literary history and the varied beauty of its literary forms, the rich theology which it embodies and proclaims, its implications for faith and ethics in today's world -- all this and more has scarcely been touched upon in this study guide. Do not think that because you have laid in a few boards and nails and acquired some structural plans you can now relax in your house!

On the other hand, if you are seriously interested in building the Bible into your life, or more importantly, in building your life upon the God of the Bible in the community of faith which gave birth to the Bible and still lives from it, then *Mastering Old Testament Facts* will provide you some indispensable building materials.

It is the authors' wish that on this trip to the lumber yard you will meet the Architect who can be found there and seize the opportunity to inquire how best to get on with your building.

UNIT I: INTRODUCTION TO THE OLD TESTAMENT

OBJECTIVES

After completion of Unit 1, you will be able to do the following:

1. Define the word canon as used in connection with the Old Testament.

2. Name three major forms of the Old Testament canon in historical order.

3. Identify three canon forms by labeling six descriptions.

4. Name the three major divisions of the Jewish Scriptures.

5. Name the four major divisions of the Christian Old Testament.

6. State the number of books in the Protestant Old Testament.

7. Distinguish between the terms apocryphal and deuterocanonical as applied to Old Testament writings.

8. Name at least three Old Testament literary types other than canonical categories.

9. Identify at least two passages as to literary type.

10. Identify the relationship between canonical categories and literary types in the Old Testament.

11. Identify some major literary types in the first two divisions of the Christian Old Testament.

12. State at least two reasons for studying the Old Testament as literature.

13. Identify three possible meanings of the term Old Testament history.

14. Order chronologically and/or date ten key events in the history of Israel.

15. Number in chronological order seven major periods in the history of Israel.

16. Associate at least ten persons with the key events or the periods in which these events took place.

You may already know some of these without studying Unit 1. The Unit 1 pre-test will tell you how much of this material you know before you begin. You are not expected to do well on this test because you have not yet studied the material. However, by taking the test you will become acquainted with the types of questions and information you will be working on in the unit. You will also be able to compare your present knowledge with your achievement after studying the unit, and thus measure that growth.

Now begin the pre-test on the next page.

A. CANON

Fill in the blanks:

1. A list of writings accepted as Sacred Scripture by a religious community is called the _____.

Name three major forms of the Old Testament canon:

2._____

3._____

4._____

The three major divisions of the Jewish Scriptures are:

5._____

6._____

7._____

The four major divisions of the Christian Old Testament are:

8._____

9._____

10._____

11._____

Circle the letter of the ONE BEST answer.

12. The number of books in the Protestant Old Testament is:
    a. 24
    b. 39
    c. 46
    d. 66

13. Protestants call the books included in the Catholic Old Testament, but usually omitted from their own:
    a. spurious
    b. apocalyptic
    c. pseudonymous
    d. apocryphal

14. Catholics call the books in their Old Testament, but not in the Jewish or Protestant:
    a. doubtful
    b. deuterocanonical
    c. apocryphal
    d. anonymous

B. LITERATURE

Circle the letter of the ONE BEST answer.

1. ALL of the following statements are valid reasons to study the Old Testament as literature EXCEPT:
    a. Sacred Scripture, including the Old Testament, is always of high literary quality.
    b. The Old Testament is a collection of the finest literature of ancient Israel.
    c. In the King James Version, the Old Testament has shaped and nourished the English language.
    d. The Old Testament is one of the literary treasures of the entire human race.

2. ONE of the following lists contains ONLY Old Testament LITERARY TYPES:
    a. saga, annal, prophetic oracle, victory song
    b. elegy, sonnet, thanksgiving song, court history
    c. poetry, wisdom, law, history
    d. ode, epic, ballad, quatrain

3. ONE of the following lists contains ONLY Old Testament CANONICAL CATEGORIES:
    a. wisdom, proverb, parable, psalm
    b. psalm, pentateuch, oracle, wisdom
    c. pentateuch, historical books, poetry and wisdom, prophetic writings
    d. victory song, thanksgiving song, work song, funeral song

4. ALL of the following statements are true EXCEPT:
    a. "Canonical category" and "literary type" are different but related terms.
    b. The names of the canonical divisions are very general literary categories.
    c. "Literary type" is a much more specific category than "canonical division."
    d. The name of a canonical division is a useful guide to the literary type of each passage in it.

5. ALL of the following statements are true
   EXCEPT:
   a. The historical books include many literary
      types.
   b. All the songs in the Old Testament are in
      the book of Psalms.
   c. The Old Testament contains fables.
   d. The Pentateuch contains both history and
      law.

6. Balaam's pronouncements in Numbers 23 and
   Hannah's prayer in 1 Samuel 2 are examples
   of the following specific literary types:
   a. fable and history
   b. song and fable
   c. history and oracle
   d. oracle and thanksgiving song

C. HISTORY

1. To complete the following statement most
   appropriately, place ONE of these words in
   EACH of the blanks below: world, Israel,
   language, religion, God, writings, laws,
   canon.

   History of _____, history of the
   _____, and history of the _____
   are all possible meanings of the term "Old
   Testament history."

2. Number the following events in chronological
   order from 1 to 10.
   _____David takes Jerusalem
   _____Edict of Cyrus
   _____Call of Abraham
   _____Maccabean revolt
   _____Exodus
   _____Fall of Samaria
   _____Alexander the Great
   _____Fall of Jerusalem
   _____Josiah's deuteronomic reform
   _____Zerubbabel's temple

3. Write the letter of EACH SET OF DATES (right
   column) in the blank before the PERIOD (left
   column) it defines:
   1. ____Persian period   a) c.1950–c.1550 B.C.
   2. ____In Egypt   b) c.1650–c.1250 B.C.
   3. ____Monarchy   c) c.1250–c.1000 B.C.
   4. ____Ancestors   d) c.1000–587 B.C.
   5. ____Greek period   e) 587–538 B.C.
   6. ____Judges   f) 538–333 B.C.
   7. ____Exile   g) 333–63 B.C.

4. Write the letter of EACH EVENT or PERIOD
   (right column) in the blank before the
   PERSON (left column) with whom it is
   most closely associated.
   1. ____David   a) Exodus
   2. ____Zerubbabel   b) Edict ending the Exile
   3. ____Cyrus   c) Patriarchs
   4. ____Josiah   d) Deuteronomic reform
   5. ____Moses   e) Monarchy
   6. ____Abraham   f) Building of Second
                               Temple
   7. ____Alexander   g) Judges
   8. ____Nebuchadnezzar   h) Revolt against Greeks
   9. ____Joshua   i) Fall of Jerusalem
   10. ___Judas Maccabeus   j) Greek Period

Check answers on page 100. Compute scores on page 104 and enter on the growth record for Unit 1, page 106.

INSTRUCTIONS

Unit 1 is different from all the other units in that the text is not the Bible but Unit 1 itself. The left-hand side of each page contains the text, while the main ideas of the text are presented graphically on the right-hand side of each page.

1. Read the text on the left.

2. Note the main ideas on the right.

3. Complete as much of the self-check as you can from memory.

4. If necessary, go back to the text to review whatever was missed.

5. Complete the self-check from memory.

6. Check your answers. (You will find the answers at the bottom of the page, upside down.)

7. After completing each section, take the section test that follows each section. Check answers, compute your score and enter it on growth record as directed.

8. Take the unit test and correct it. Compute and record score as directed.

9. Look up references of items that were missed. Relevant pages are given after answers for each section. In this way you will complete your mastery of Unit 1.

SECTION 1: OLD TESTAMENT CANON

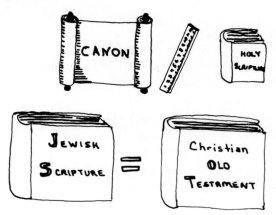

The list of writings accepted as Sacred Scripture by a religious community is called the CANON. Canon means "measuring rod." This refers to the standards used in deciding which books to include.

Christians include the JEWISH SCRIPTURES in the Bible and call them the OLD TESTAMENT. However, there are slight differences in the lists of books accepted by Jews, by Catholics, and by Protestants.

These differences are of two main kinds: WHICH BOOKS are included and how they are ARRANGED.

We shall look at the three forms of the Old Testament in historical order.

SELF-CHECK 1

Circle the letter of the ONE BEST answer:

1. When applied to the Bible, the word "canon" means:
    a. A large gun used by field artillery units in the army.
    b. A list of writings accepted as Sacred Scripture.
    c. An ordained churchman connected with a cathedral.
    d. A body of church law.

2. The original meaning of canon, "measuring rod," referred to:
    a. The length of the list of books in the Bible.
    b. The church official who enforced the authority of the Bible.
    c. The religious body which resolved debates about the Scripture.
    d. The standards used in deciding which books to include in the Bible.

Fill in the blanks:

3. The three main forms of the Old Testament canon are _____, _____, and _____.

4. The two main differences among these three canons are (a) which_____ are included and (b) how they are _____.

Answers: 1,b; 2,d; 3, Jewish, Catholic, and Protestant; 4, (a) books or writings; (b) arranged.

7

The Jewish canon is arranged in three main parts:
the LAW, the PROPHETS, and the WRITINGS. In Hebrew,
these three parts are called Torah, Neviim, and
Kesuvim, or TaNaK for short. Thus, what Christians
call the Old Testament, Jews call the TANAK. It
constitutes the entire Jewish Bible.

The second part of the Tanak, is sub-divided into
FORMER PROPHETS and LATTER PROPHETS.

All of the writings are combined and counted in
such a way as to number TWENTY-FOUR (24) books:

The LAW (Torah)

    Genesis

    Exodus

    Leviticus

    Numbers

    Deuteronomy

The PROPHETS (Neviim)

FORMER PROPHETS	LATTER PROPHETS
Joshua	Isaiah
Judges	Jeremiah
Samuel	Ezekiel
Kings	The Twelve

The WRITINGS (Kesuvim)

Psalms	FIVE FESTAL SCROLLS:
Job	Ruth
Proverbs	Song of Songs
Daniel	Ecclesiastes
Ezra-Nehemiah	Lamentations
Chronicles	Esther

This selection of books, in this order, was made
by Jews in Palestine shortly after the time of
Jesus Christ. It is sometimes called the Hebrew
canon, for it contained only books originally
written in Hebrew; or the Palestinian canon,
because it was the Bible of Jews in Palestine.

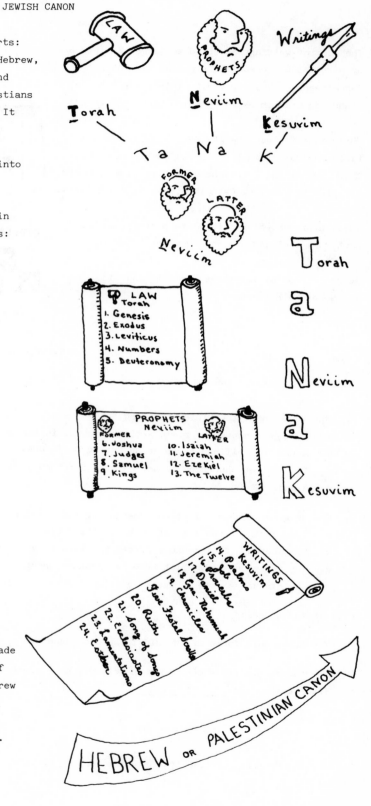

8

Jesus knew these books as Scripture, though during his lifetime there was still some debate about which books to include in the third part (the Writings).

JEWISH CANON (24 BOOKS)		
HEBREW OR PALESTINE CANON		
TANAK		
LAW	PROPHETS	WRITINGS
Torah	Neviim	Kesuvim
	FORMER LATTER	

SELF-CHECK 2

Complete blanks:

1. The three main parts of the Jewish Canon are _____, _____, and_____ (use English terms).

2. The second part is divided into _____ _____, and _____ _____.

3. The total number of books in the Tanak, or Jewish Bible, is_____.

CATHOLIC CANON

In the centuries just before, during, and after the life of Christ, many Jews used Greek as their first language. Jews in and around Alexandria, Egypt translated the Hebrew Scriptures into Greek. They included some books that were originally written in Greek.

Early Christians used this Greek version of the Old Testament. It was the Greek canon which Catholic Christians translated into Latin. For this reason, the CATHOLIC CANON is sometimes called the "GREEK AND LATIN CANON" because it was the Bible of Jews in Alexandria and other Greek-speaking cities.

The Greek and Latin canon differed from the Hebrew canon in two important ways.

First, it was arranged in four main parts instead of three, with many of the books in different order.

These four main parts are:

    PENTATEUCH (or Law)

    HISTORICAL BOOKS (or History)

    POETRY AND WISDOM (or Poetry)

    PROPHETIC WRITINGS (or Prophecy)

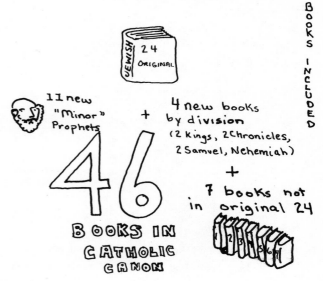

Second, it included seven entire books not in the Jewish or Hebrew canon, as well as several additions to the Hebrew canonical books. These writings, equally inspired in the Catholic view, are called "DEUTEROCANONICAL" because they were later added to the canon. The additional titles are:

    Tobit   Wisdom of Solomon

    Judith   Ecclesiasticus

    1 Maccabees   Baruch

    2 Maccabees

Also, by counting each of "The Twelve" (Minor Prophets) as a separate book, and by dividing Samuel, Kings, Chronicles, and Ezra-Nehemiah into two books each, the Catholic canon arrived at a total of FORTY-SIX (46) books.

SELF-CHECK 3

Circle the letter of the ONE BEST answer:

1. The four main parts of the Catholic Old Testament canon are:
    a. Pentateuch, Poetry, Prophecy, and Apocalypse
    b. Law, Former Prophets, Latter Prophets, and Writings
    c. Law, History, Prophecy, Deuterocanonical Books
    d. Pentateuch, Historical Books, Poetry and Wisdom, and Prophetic Writings

2. The books in the Catholic canon but not in the Jewish canon are called:
    a. Spurious books
    b. Anonymous works
    c. Deuterocanonical books
    d. Maccabees

3. The number of books in the Catholic Old Testament is:
    a. 24
    b. 36
    c. 39
    d. 46

Answers: 1,d; 2,c; 3,d.

At the time of the Reformation, the Protestant insistence on the supreme authority of Scripture reopened the question of exactly what books belong in the Bible. Protestants admitted only the writings found in the Jewish (Hebrew) canon.

The writings Catholics call "Deuterocanonical" are called "APOCRYPHAL" by Protestants. They are excluded from the canon, but are printed in some Protestant Bibles at the end of the Old Testament.

Protestants kept the four main categories of the Catholic canon, as well as the order and way of counting books. The Protestant canon, therefore, combines the JEWISH CHOICE of books and the CATHOLIC ARRANGEMENT of them.

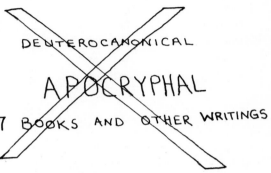

The result is an Old Testament of THIRTY-NINE books, arranged as follows:

PENTATEUCH (5)

Genesis

Exodus

Leviticus

Numbers

Deuteronomy

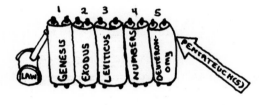

$$46 - 7 = 39$$

HISTORICAL BOOKS (12)

Joshua	1 and 2 Chronicles
Judges	Ezra
Ruth	Nehemiah
1 and 2 Samuel	Esther
1 and 2 Kings	

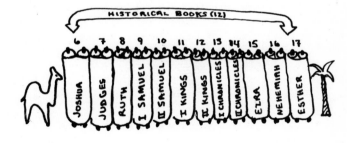

POETRY AND WISDOM (5)

Job

Psalms

Proverbs

Ecclesiastes

Song of Solomon

11

PROPHETIC WRITINGS (17)

    Major Prophets:

      Isaiah   Ezekiel

      Jeremiah   Daniel

      Lamentations

    Minor Prophets:

      Hosea   Nahum

      Joel   Habakkuk

      Amos   Zephaniah

      Obadiah   Haggai

      Jonah   Zechariah

      Micah   Malachi

Mastering Old Testament Facts will follow the Protestant canon, devoting one volume to each of the four canonical divisions.

SELF–CHECK 4

Complete blanks:

1.   The Protestant canon combines the _____ choice of which books to include and the _____ arrangement of them.

2.   The writings called "Deuterocanonical" by Catholics are called _____ by Protestants.

3.   Writings that Jews group under one title as the book of "The Twelve" are counted as twelve separate books by both Catholics and Protestants and called the _____ Prophets.

4.   The total number of books in the Protestant canon is_____.

JUST FOR FUN!

See how long it takes you to memorize the thirty-nine books of the Protestant Old Testament, in the categories and order of the Christian (Catholic <u>and</u> Protestant) canon.

Answers: 1. Jewish, Catholic; 2. "Apocryphal"; 3. Minor; 4. 39.

SECTION TEST I

Circle the letter of the ONE BEST answer:

1. The three major forms of the Old Testament canon, in historical order, are:

   a. Protestant, Catholic, Jewish

   b. Catholic, Jewish, Protestant

   c. Jewish, Protestant, Catholic

   d. Jewish, Catholic, Protestant

2. The Tanak is ALL of the following EXCEPT:

   a. What Jews call the Bible

   b. The Jewish name for what Christians call the Old Testament

   c. A scroll containing the five books of Moses

   d. An abbreviation for Torah, Neviim, and Kesuvim

3. ALL of the following are apocryphal books EXCEPT:

   a. Ecclesiasticus

   b. 1 Maccabees

   c. 2 Chronicles

   d. Wisdom of Solomon

4. The books called by Jews "Former Prophets" (Joshua - 2 Kings) are called by Christians:

   a. Pentateuch

   b. Historical Books

   c. Poetry and Wisdom

   d. Prophetic Writings

5. All of the following terms designate the first five books in the Bible EXCEPT:

   a. Law

   b. Pentateuch

   c. Tanak

   d. Torah

6. ALL of the following terms are synonymous EXCEPT:

   a. Catholic canon

   b. Greek and Latin canon

   c. Alexandrian canon

   d. Hebrew canon

7. ALL of the following terms refer to the Tanak EXCEPT:

   a. Christian canon

   b. Jewish canon

   c. Hebrew canon

   d. Palestinian canon

8. "The Twelve" as used in connection with the Old Testament canon refers to:

   a. The minor prophets

   b. The tribes of Israel

   c. The apostles of Jesus

   d. The sons of Jacob

Write the letter of EACH phrase in the right column in the blank before the ONE item in the left column with which it is MOST closely associated. Use each letter only once.

9.___39 books

10.___Apocryphal books

11.___Alexandrian canon

12.___Earliest form of Old Testament

13.___Tanak

a. Deuterocanonical books

b. Catholic Old Testament

c. Protestant Old Testament

d. Torah, Neviim, Kesuvim

e. Jewish canon

Fill in the blanks to complete the following statements:

"Canon" as used in connection with the Old Testament means a (14) _____ of writings accepted as (15) _____ by a religious community. Christians divide the Old Testament into (16) _____, (17) _____, (18)_____, and (19) _____.

20. Old Testament books not in the Jewish canon, called "deuterocanonical" by Catholics, are called _____by Protestants.

Check your answers on page 100. Compute your score on page 104 and enter on the growth record for Unit 1 on page 106. After studying any items missed, begin Section 2 on the next page.

The Sacred Scriptures defined by the Old Testament canon are also a body of great LITERATURE. These writings are a collection of the FINEST LITERATURE of ancient ISRAEL.

Modern Israelis study portions of the Hebrew Old Testament in school much as English-speaking students read and learn Shakespeare. It is an anthology of masterpieces of Hebrew language and culture, written and collected over a thousand-year period. The Old Testament is one of the LITERARY TREASURES of the HUMAN RACE.

Even in English translations, this literature retains its beauty and power. The KING JAMES VERSION of the Old and New Testaments has helped to shape and nourish the ENGLISH LANGUAGE for more than three centuries.

Generation after generation, millions of people have memorized portions of the Old Testament in English. Although memorization is not an objective of *Mastering Old Testament Facts*, a few passages that are frequently memorized will be indicated as a suggestion. You will not be tested on memorization of these passages, but you may wish to learn them just for fun.

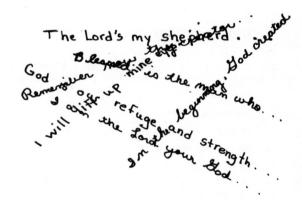

LITERARY TYPES

The Old Testament contains a rich variety of types of literature.

The commonly used terms for the canonical divisions (law, history, poetry, prophecy) represent very general literary categories.

These canonical categories can be misleading, however, if they are used to define the LITERARY TYPE of any particular passage. That is one reason you are learning terms that differ slightly from the short, commonly used ones.

14

The PENTATEUCH (Genesis – Deuteronomy), for instance, is often called the "Law." It does contain the basic Law of ancient Israel· and many passages of legal material. But the Hebrew word "Torah," often translated as "Law," in its broader meaning connotes "revelation." The Torah or Pentateuch contains not only laws, but also the earliest traditions of Israel's history, as well as some outstanding examples of poetry (e.g. the VICTORY SONG of Miriam in Exodus 15) and of prophecy (e.g. the ORACLES of Balaam in Numbers 22--24). It would be a mistake to think that the first five books of the Bible are all legal material.

PENTATEUCH - LAW
↓
Hebrew TORAH connotes "Revelation"
+
Poetry (such as Victory Song of Miriam)
+
Prophecy (such as Oracles of Balaam)

Similarly, the HISTORICAL BOOKS contain many literary types other than annals of history. For example, the two great cycles of prophetic material concerning Elijah (1 Kings 17--19,21) and Elisha (2 Kings 1--9), magnificent poems such as the THANKSGIVING SONG of Hannah (1 Samuel 2:1-10) and David's ELEGY (or FUNERAL SONG) over Saul and Jonathan (2 Samuel 1:17-27), wisdom types such as Nathan's PARABLE (2 Samuel 12:1-4), Jotham's FABLE (Judges 9:8-15), and Samson's RIDDLE (Judges 14:14) are all to be found in the HISTORICAL BOOKS. In addition, the historical narratives themselves, both in the Pentateuch and in the Historical Books, include many specific literary types. Some of these (such as ANNALS, COURT HISTORY, and LETTERS) are "historical" in the modern sense. Others (such as MYTH, LEGEND, and SAGA) tell the truth about life, but do not purport to be factual reports of an eye-witness.

HISTORICAL BOOKS
⇩
History
+
Prophetic Material
+
Poetry
(Hannah's "Thanksgiving Song")
(David's "Elegy")
+
Wisdom Types
(Jotham's FABLE)
(Samson's RIDDLE)
+
Annals
Court History
Letters
Myth
Legend
Saga

To summarize: The canonical categories, though they describe broadly the kind of literature in each of the four sections of the Old Testament, cannot be used to determine the literary type of a particular passage.

Since *Mastering Old Testament Facts* seeks only to help you learn content, the guided reading will seldom call attention to the specific literary type of the passage you are reading. However, some of the "Just for Funs" will focus on literary type as a way to appreciate the flavor and function of the text.

Check the terms which ARE literary types in the Old Testament but ARE NOT canonical categories:

1. _____Poetry   6. _____Fable
2. _____Quatrain   7. _____History
3. _____Victory song   8. _____Thanksgiving song
4. _____Law   9. _____Sonnet
5. _____Oracle   10. _____Riddle

Circle the letter of the ONE BEST answer:

11. The commonly used terms for the four divisions of the Christian Old Testament (Law, History, Poetry, Prophecy) are:

    a. Very general literary categories
    b. Very precise theological categories
    c. A useful guide to the literary type of passages in each division
    d. Terms which have little to do with the content of each division

12. Modern Israelis study the Old Testament in school for ALL of the following reasons EXCEPT:

    a. It is a collection of the finest literature of ancient Israel.
    b. Synagogue leaders require that it be studied in public schools.
    c. It includes masterpieces of Hebrew language and culture.
    d. It is one of the literary treasures of the entire human race.

13. The Old Testament has had a formative influence on English language and literature through:
    a. Shakespeare
    b. The Living Bible
    c. Jews of England and America
    d. The King James Version of the Bible

14. ALL of the following statements are true EXCEPT:
    a. Canonical categories can be used to define the literary type of a particular passage.
    b. The Old Testament contains a rich variety of literary types.
    c. Millions of people have memorized portions of the Old Testament.
    d. Two great prophetic cycles are found in the Historical Books.

15. ALL of the following are Old Testament literary types EXCEPT:

    a. Elegy
    b. Saga
    c. Canon
    d. Court history

Check answers on page 100. Compute your score on page 104 and enter it on the growth record for Unit 1 on page 106. After studying any items missed, begin Section 3 on the next page.

"Old Testament history" can refer to at least three different things:

1. History of Israel
2. History of the writings in the Old Testament
3. History of the canon

While mastering Old Testament facts, you should be careful not to confuse the time an EVENT in the Old Testament took place (history of Israel) with the time the ACCOUNT of the event was WRITTEN (history of the writings) or with the time this writing came to be viewed as SCRIPTURE (history of the canon).

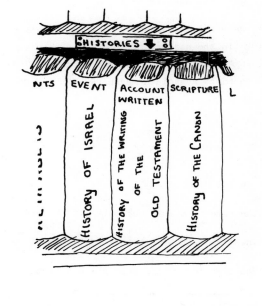

Although these three histories are distinct, they are CLOSELY RELATED. The history of the CANON depends upon the history of the WRITINGS. The date any book is "canonized" as Sacred Scripture is always later than the date it is written -- sometimes several centuries later.

Canonization is also closely related to the history of ISRAEL. Particular historical events often caused a growing dependence on certain writings as Word of God and led to the drawing up of an official list of authoritative books.

The history of the WRITINGS is also imbedded in the history of ISRAEL in several ways.

Many Old Testament passages narrate a specific historical event or respond to a specific event with some word of interpretation or judgment or promise.

Sometimes a specific event caused God's people to remember and retell the story of an earlier, related event (such as the Exodus, or the stories about David). The way the early story is retold may be influenced by the later circumstances.

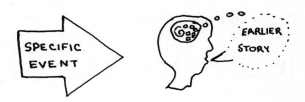

Since some acquaintance with the history of Israel is basic to mastering Old Testament facts, you will be tested on your knowledge of ten key EVENTS. These will serve as mental pegs on which to hang other Old Testament facts.

These dates will enable you to identify six major PERIODS in the history of Israel. As you work through *Mastering Old Testament Facts,* you will also learn to associate major PERSONS and BOOKS with them.

SELF-CHECK 1

Fill in the blanks:

1. The time of EVENTS recounted in the Old Testament belongs to the history of _____.

2. The time ACCOUNTS in the Old Testament were WRITTEN belongs to the history of the _____.

3. The time the writings in the Old Testament came to be viewed as SCRIPTURE belongs to the history of the _____.

EVENTS

The two fundamental events around which we can best organize Israel's history are the EXODUS and the EXILE.

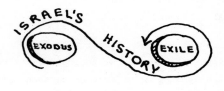

All that occurred before the Exodus may be called pre-history or proto-history. Examples of pre-history are the events recounted in the first eleven chapters of Genesis, including the Creation (Adam and Eve) and the Flood (Noah).

In chapter 12 of Genesis, there is a sudden change of pace when the story focuses on ABRAHAM. As a figure in Israel's proto-history, Abraham can be dated only in a very general and approximate way. The time limits within which Abraham must have lived are:

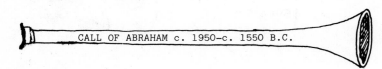

CALL OF ABRAHAM c. 1950–c. 1550 B.C.

Abraham's grandson, JACOB (also named Israel), migrated to Egypt with all his family. His descendants, the Hebrews, stayed IN EGYPT for about four hundred years until the Exodus.

The EXODUS (Greek for "the way out") refers to MOSES leading the descendants of Jacob (Israel) out of Egypt. After forty years in the wilderness or DESERT, JOSHUA led the next generation across the Jordan River into Canaan (the CONQUEST). The Exodus, desert, and conquest cannot be dated exactly, but they probably all occurred in the thirteenth century B.C. For convenience, remember 1250 B.C. as the approximate date of the Exodus. Using "c." (Latin "circa") to stand for "approximately," remember:

EXODUS   c. 1250 B.C.

SELF-CHECK 2

A. Fill in the dates:

Call of Abraham   (1) c._____ –c._____ B.C.

Exodus   (2) c._____ B.C.

B. Number the following persons in chronological order:

_____ Noah   _____ Abraham

_____ Moses   _____ Joshua

_____ Adam and Eve   _____ Jacob

That takes care of two dates to remember. The next four fall between the Exodus and the Exile during the 700 years that constitute the heart of the history of ancient Israel. After some two hundred years of loose confederation under the leadership of judges, Israel sought greater stability and national identity under a king.

ISRAEL

Answers: A. (1) c. 1950–c. 1550 B.C.; (2) c. 1250 B.C. B. 2,5,1;3,6,4.

19

Although SAUL was Israel's first king, the founder
of the monarchy in Jerusalem was DAVID. David was
first made king of the southern tribes in Hebron.
Later, northern leaders loyal to the house of Saul
grew tired of Saul's inept son and asked David to
be king over all Israel. Seeking a neutral site,
David seized the Jebusite city of JERUSALEM and
made it capital of the kingdom which he created by
military and political skill. Remember:

 — DAVID TAKES JERUSALEM — c. 1000 B.C.

The Kingdom of Israel was united and prosperous
during the long reigns of David and his son, SOLOMON.
Just after Solomon's death (c. 922), the ten northern
tribes seceded and formed the NORTHERN KINGDOM, sometimes
called Samaria (after its capital city) or Ephraim
(after its main tribe) or simply ISRAEL. It lasted
two hundred years, a lifespan which should not be
hard for Americans to remember near the year of
their bicentennial.

Tyrannized for years by the military might of
Assyria, its end was marked by the:

FALL OF SAMARIA — 721 B.C.

The Northern Kingdom took the name Israel; but
the SOUTHERN KINGDOM kept the Davidic dynasty in-
tact on the throne in Jerusalem. This kingdom
included only the tribes of Benjamin and Judah, and
is usually called simply JUDAH.

Just one century after the fall of Samaria, King JOSIAH
of Judah set out to restore the Temple which Solomon
had built in Jerusalem but which had fallen into dis-
repair during the idolatrous reign of Josiah's father,
Manasseh. During the renovation, a book of the
ancient covenant law of Israel was found in the
Temple...probably an early version of the Book of
DEUTERONOMY. The king called the people to the

Temple for a ceremony of covenant renewal and set
out to reform the whole life of the nation in line
with the teachings of this book. This key event of
the seventh century B.C. is called:

REFORM
621 BC

```
┣━━━━━━━━━━━━━━━━━━━━━━━━━━━━━━━━━━━━━━━┫
     JOSIAH's DEUTERONOMIC REFORM - 621 B.C.
┣━━━━━━━━━━━━━━━━━━━━━━━━━━━━━━━━━━━━━━━┫
```

During Josiah's reign, the Assyrian empire crumbled
and Egypt moved north to gobble up the pieces. In
605 B.C. the Babylonians defeated Egypt at Carchemish
and continued to expand west and south. NEBUCHADNEZZAR,
king of Babylon, captured Jerusalem in 598 B.C.,
deported the ruling classes of Judah, and installed
a vassal king. About ten years later, Judah dared
to try to throw off the Babylonian yoke; in 587 B.C.
Nebuchadnezzar's army again took Jerusalem, burned
Solomon's Temple and the royal palace, deported
more captives and put an end to the monarchy in
Israel. The event and date to remember:

```
┌─────────────────────────────────────┐
│      FALL OF JERUSALEM - 587 B.C.    │
└─────────────────────────────────────┘
```

This event marks the beginning of the second great
landmark in Israel's history, the EXILE in the sixth
century B.C.

by NEBUCHADNEZZAR

SELF-CHECK 3

A. Fill in the dates of events between the Exodus and the Exile:

    1. The monarchy - David takes Jerusalem   c._____ B.C.

    2. Fall of Samaria   _____ B.C.

    3. Josiah's Deuteronomic Reform   _____ B.C.

    4. Fall of Jerusalem   _____ B.C.

B. Number the following persons in chronological order:

    _____ Solomon   _____ Nebuchadnezzar

    _____ David   _____ Josiah

    _____ Joshua   _____ Saul

Answers: A. 1. 1000 B.C.; 2. 721 B.C.; 3. 621 B.C.; 4. 587 B.C. B. 4,3,1; 6,5,2

The EXILE lasted about a lifetime, often referred
to in round numbers as forty years. It was actually
forty-nine years later when Cyrus, king of Persia,
overran Babylon and permitted the Jews to return to
Jerusalem. This event marks the end of the Exile and
is one of the four remaining dates to remember:

EDICT OF CYRUS - 538 B.C.

When a remnant of the former Kingdom of Judah, from
then on called "the Jews," returned to Jerusalem
in 538 B.C., a top priority was to rebuild the
Temple. This was done by ZERUBBABEL, a descendant
of David, who was appointed governor by the PERSIANS.
The second Temple is therefore sometimes called
Zerubbabel's Temple. Remember the date:

ZERUBBABEL's TEMPLE - 515 B.C.

For about two hundred years after the Exile,
the Jews lived under Persian rule in a province
which the Persians called "Beyond the River."
They spoke Aramaic and enjoyed considerable peace
but little prosperity.

The eastern conquests of Alexander of Macedonia,
called the Great, ended the Persian empire and
introduced the Greek language as a universal
medium of communication. A convenient date to
remember is:

α   ALEXANDER THE GREAT - c. 333 B.C.   ∩

Alexander's followers, first those in Egypt then
those in Syria, allowed the Jews relative freedom
for many years. Then the Syrian ruler, Antiochus
Epiphanes, set out to Hellenize the Jews, even if
it meant destroying Judaism. He went so far as to
outlaw Judaism and to profane the Temple with swine
and pagan gods.

PROFANED   TEMPLE

The Jews revolted in 167 B.C. under a leader called
JUDAS MACCABEUS. They took control of Jerusalem,
rededicated the Temple in 165 B.C., and instituted
a century of Jewish independence until the Romans
took control of Jerusalem in 63 B.C. The date to
remember is:

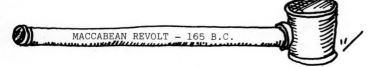

MACCABEAN REVOLT – 165 B.C.

Perhaps it will help to see these ten key events
and their dates at a single glance:

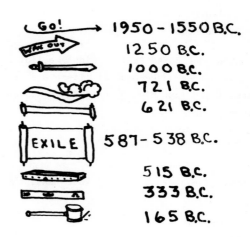

CALL OF ABRAHAM	c. 1950–c. 1550 B.C.
EXODUS	c. 1250 B.C.
DAVID TAKES JERUSALEM	c. 1000 B.C.
FALL OF SAMARIA	721 B.C.
JOSIAH's REFORM	621 B.C.
FALL OF JERUSALEM	587 B.C.
EXILE	
EDICT OF CYRUS	538 B.C.
ZERUBBABEL's TEMPLE	515 B.C.
ALEXANDER THE GREAT	333 B.C.
MACCABEAN REVOLT	165 B.C.

SELF-CHECK 4

After you have studied the above list of dates, cover it with your hand and complete the self-check
from memory.

A. Fill in the dates of events after the Exile:
1. Edict of Cyrus   _____B.C.
2. Zerubbabel builds the second Temple   _____B.C.
3. Alexander the Great conquers Persia   _____B.C.
4. Maccabean revolt   _____B.C.

B. Number the following events in chronological order:
_____Edict of Cyrus
_____David takes Jerusalem
_____Josiah's reform
_____Maccabean revolt
_____Fall of Samaria

Answers: A. 1. 538 B.C.; 2. 515 B.C.; 3. 333 B.C.; 4. 165 B.C. B. 4,1,3,5,2.

PERIODS

Seven major periods in Israel's history as told in
the Old Testament can be fixed by reference to these
same dates:

ANCESTORS	c. 1950–c. 1550 B.C.	
EGYPT	c. 1650–c. 1250 B.C.	
JUDGES	c. 1250–c. 1000 B.C.	
MONARCHY	c. 1000–587 B.C.	
EXILE	587–538 B.C.	
PERSIAN PERIOD	538–333 B.C.	
GREEK PERIOD	333– 63 B.C.	

An eighth, the ROMAN PERIOD, might be listed, but
that would take us beyond the literature of the Old
Testament and into history covered in *Mastering New
Testament Facts*.

SELF-CHECK 5

A. Cover the above list with your hand, then number the following periods in chronological order:

_____ Persian period

_____ Judges

_____ Exile

_____ Egypt

_____ Greek period

_____ Ancestors

_____ Monarchy

B. Using the first letter(s) of each period, indicate in the blank before each of the following persons
the period to which he belongs: (Example: __P.P.__ Cyrus)

_____ David

_____ Abraham

_____ Joshua

_____ Judas Maccabeus

_____ Nebuchadnezzar

Fill in the blanks:

1. The history of Israel treats the time of _____ recounted in the Old Testament.

2. The history of the writings (or literature) of the Old Testament treats the time the _____
   were _____.

3. The history of the Old Testament canon treats the time these writings came to be viewed as _____
   _____.

List and date ten key <u>events</u> in the history of Israel:

<u>Event</u>	<u>Date</u>
1. _____	_____
2. _____	_____
3. _____	_____
4. _____	_____
5. _____	_____
6. _____	_____
7. _____	_____
8. _____	_____
9. _____	_____
10. _____	_____

Number the following <u>persons</u> in chronological order:

_____ Zerubbabel   _____ Noah   _____ Judas Maccabeus

_____ Josiah   _____ Moses

Write the letter of the ONE most appropriate period or event in the blank before EACH of the following persons:

1. _____ Nebuchadnezzar   a. Greek period

2. _____ Saul   b. Monarchy

3. _____ Alexander the Great   c. Pre-history

4. _____ Abraham   d. Fall of Jerusalem

5. _____ Adam and Eve   e. Ancestors

List seven major <u>periods</u> in the history of Israel:

1. _____
2. _____
3. _____
4. _____
5. _____
6. _____
7. _____

Check answers on page 100. Compute your score on page 104 and enter it on the growth record for Unit 1 on page 106. After studying any items missed, take Unit Test 1 on the next page.

UNIT TEST I: INTRODUCTION TO THE OLD TESTAMENT

Review all three section tests before you start this unit test.

A. CANON

Complete from memory the following statements:

1. "Canon," as applied to the Old Testament means

_____.

2. The three major forms of the Old Testament canon are _____.

3. The three major divisions of the Jewish Scriptures are _____.

4. The four major divisions of the Christian Old Testament are _____, _____, _____, and _____.

5. Seven entire books not in the Hebrew canon are called:

_____ by Catholics and are part of their canon.

_____ by Protestants and are not part of their canon.

6. The Protestant Old Testament numbers____books.

Write a J (for Jewish canon), a C (for Catholic canon), or a P (for Protestant canon) in the blank before EACH of the following descriptions to identify the form or forms of Old Testament canon which each describes. Use TWO letters in ONE of the blanks and ONE in each of the OTHERS.

1. _____ Earliest of the three forms of the Old Testament canon.

2. _____ Usually omits apocryphal books.

3. _____ Includes seven deuterocanonical books.

4. _____ Former prophets/latter prophets

5. _____ Major prophets/minor prophets

6. _____ Uses Jewish list and a Catholic arrangement of Old Testament books.

B. LITERATURE

1. Name three literary types in the Old Testament mentioned in this unit, other than the canonical categories:_____

_____

2. Insert the words "canonical category" or "literary type" in the blanks so that the statements correctly describe the relationship between these terms.

_____ indicates in general the content of each division.

_____ describes the form of a specific passage.

Write the number of the ONE PHRASE (right column) in the blank before the ONE TERM (left column) which it best describes or illustrates.

3. _____ Pentateuch   a. Jotham's story about the trees (Judges 9)

4. _____ Historical books   b. Contains history and songs as well as law

5. _____ Fable   c. Samson's challenge to the Philistines

6. _____ Riddle   d. Includes poetry and wisdom, as well as prophecy and history

State TWO REASONS for studying the Old Testament as literature.

7._____

8._____

C. HISTORY

The term "Old Testament history" can refer to:

1. The history of _____

2. The history of _____

3. The history of _____

Number in chronological order (1-7) the following periods in the history of Israel:

_____Judges   _____Persian Period

_____Ancestors

_____Monarchy   _____Exile

_____Greek period

_____Egypt

Write the letter of the appropriate DATE (right
column) in the blank before EACH EVENT (left
column):

1. _____Josiah's Deuteronomic   a)c.1950-c.1550 B.C.
           Reform

2. _____Call of Abraham   b)c.1250 B.C.

3. _____Zerubbabel builds   c)c.1000 B.C.
           second temple

4. _____Fall of Jerusalem   d)721 B.C.

5. _____Maccabean revolt   e)621 B.C.

6. _____Exodus   f)587 B.C.

7. _____Edict of Cyrus   g)538 B.C.

8. _____Fall of Samaria   h)515 B.C.

9. _____Alexander conquers   i)333 B.C.
           Persia

10. _____David takes Jerusalem   j)165 B.C.

Write the letter of EACH EVENT (right column) in the blank before the ONE PERSON (left column) with whom
it is most closely associated:

1. _____Abraham   a. Babylonian army ends Southern Kingdom

2. _____Zerubbabel   b. Monarchy established in Jerusalem

3. _____Jacob   c. Beginning of Patriarchal period

4. _____Josiah   d. Conquest of Promised Land

5. _____Nebuchadnezzar   e. Beginning of period in Egypt

6. _____Moses   f. Revolt against Greek-speaking rulers

7. _____Cyrus   g. Starts reform after finding book of law

8. _____Joshua   h. Permits Jews to return to Jerusalem

9. _____Judas Maccabeus   i. Exodus

10. _____David   j. Leads the remnant after the return to Jerusalem

*Check answers on page 100. Compute your scores on page 104 and enter them on the growth record for Unit
1 on page 106. If you scored 90% or more, you should move on to Unit 2. If you scored less than 90%,
review the parts you missed before beginning Unit 2.*

You are about to begin reading the Old Testament itself. Before you plunge into its rich details, it will be helpful to look at its first five books as a whole.

UNITY

These books _are_ a whole. The sacred story that begins with Genesis and continues through Deuteronomy was once a single holy book. Its division into five books was partly a matter of convenience: it was too long to go on one scroll.

In _Mastering Old Testament Facts_, these five books will be treated in two units. This is entirely a matter of convenience in order to fit the material into the pages available.

NAMES

The one great work that will now occupy your attention is called by various names:

- the PENTATEUCH (Greek: _pente_ "five" + _teuchos_ "tool," "scroll-case," or "scroll"), because the work was preserved on five scrolls.

- the TORAH, a Hebrew word meaning "instruction," "law," or by extension, "revelation," because this was the basic holy book to which ancient Israel looked for divine instruction in faith and practice.

- the LAW, because this is the common, though inadequate, English translation of "Torah."

- the FIVE BOOKS OF MOSES, or simply "Moses," because he is the great lawgiver and founder of Israel, whose personality dominates the work from Exodus through Deuteronomy; and because both Jewish and Christian traditions have viewed Moses as its author.

CONTENTS

In broadest terms, the Pentateuch contains two kinds of material:

1. Israel's historical traditions, from the creation to the death of Moses.

2. Israel's laws, in five great legal collections:

    The Decalogue (Exodus 20)
    The Book of the Covenant (Exodus 21--23)
    The Priestly Code (Exodus 25--Numbers 10)
    The Holiness Code (Leviticus 17--26)
    The Deuteronomic Code (Deuteronomy 12--26)

STRUCTURE

The historical and legal material in the Pentateuch is built together into a single structure. It can be outlined in simplified form as follows:

Primeval history	Genesis 1--11
Patriarchal history	Genesis 12--50
Deliverance from Egypt	Exodus 1--18
Law at Sinai	Exodus 19--Numbers 10
Guidance in the Wilderness	Numbers 10--36
Review: Deuteronomy	Deuteronomy 1--33

FLOW

This is a story that moves, so it may be helpful to visualize the unity of the Pentateuch in its flow as well as in its structure. You can do this in terms of the places where the action occurs, or in terms of a family tree of persons.

A. Geographical

Ancient Israel was a small, ethnic kingdom occupying a narrow strip of land at the crossroads of the Fertile Crescent, midway between the great empires of Mesopotamia and Egypt. Her whole history bears the imprint of interaction with those cultures. Often the interaction was like that of nut and nutcracker! But the interaction, both positive and negative, is foreshadowed in the geographical flow of the Pentateuch.

Beginning in Eden (Mesopotamia), the action moves in the person of Abraham northwest to Haran, then southwest to Canaan. The movement to Egypt is hinted at in Abraham's story, then realized in the Joseph cycle, when all the family of Jacob (Israel) migrates to that fertile land. Exodus tells of the departure from Egypt; Numbers is set in the southern desert or wilderness; and Deuteronomy brings the action to the very boundary of the promised land. Follow the flow in your mind's eye.

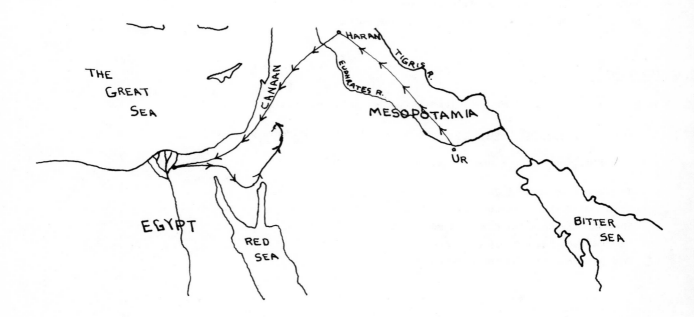

B. Genealogical

Names of persons in the Pentateuch, and especially in Genesis, often represent entire peoples or groups. Consider, for example, the following equivalents:

Adam — Humankind

Shem — Semites

Abraham — Hebrews

Jacob — Israel

Seen in this light, the genealogies of Genesis show not only the constant multiplying of peoples on the earth, but also the progressive narrowing of the story's focus from all humankind to the particular people through whom God means to reveal Himself and work out His saving purpose. The pattern is fixed in Genesis; from Exodus onward, Israel marches onto the stage of history to play out the drama of obedience and servanthood, of disobedience and disaster. The New Testament extends this pattern to a point of convergence in the single person of Jesus Christ, and then the flow moves back outward. See how the pattern is established in the Pentateuch:

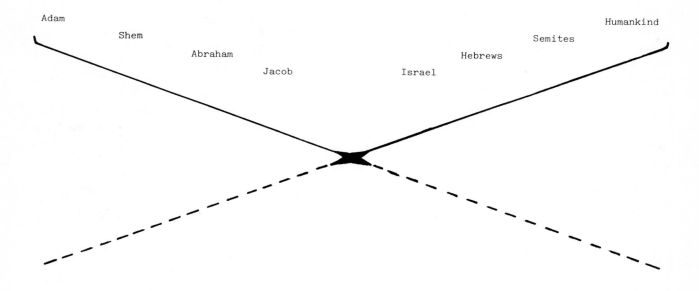

You may prefer to visualize the unifying flow of the Pentateuch in another way after you have read it. You will not be tested on the material in this introduction unless it reappears later. It is included here to provide an overall framework for the particularities which you will be invited to observe in Units 2 and 3.

UNIT 2: GENESIS AND EXODUS

OBJECTIVES

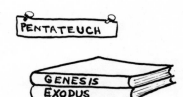

In Unit 2, the learnings have been classified according to three
major categories to help you learn more easily and to know what
you are learning. They are: structure, narrative, and features.

Upon completion of Unit 2, you will be able to do the following:

1. State the headings of the major divisions in Genesis and Exodus.
2. Number in sequence 14 events in Genesis and Exodus.
3. Identify the relationships, as mate or child, of 9 men to 8 women.
4. Associate at least 16 events with 16 men who were strongly involved in them.
5. Associate at least 10 events with 10 women who were involved in them.
6. Identify at least 16 places mentioned in Genesis and Exodus.
7. Distinguish between traditional and modern views of the composition of these books.
8. Differentiate between Genesis and Exodus for at least 10 features or special content items.

In Unit 2 as in all units of this series, you are asked to take a pre-test in order to help you learn. If
you score 90% or more, you may move directly to Unit 3. However, most people will make a very low score
on the pre-test, since it tests material yet to be studied. Just taking the test will teach you some
facts, but its major value is in centering your attention on certain facts as you read Genesis and Exodus.
In addition, at the end of the unit you will have the pleasure of seeing how much you have gained in
factual knowledge.

Now begin the pre-test for Unit 2.

PRE-TEST FOR UNIT 2

A. STRUCTURE

Outlines. Circle the letter of the ONE BEST answer.

1. Genesis has two major divisions:

    a. Creation , Fall

    b. Beginnings of humanity, Beginnings of Israel

    c. Beginnings of universe, Beginnings of people

    d. Covenant, Slavery in Egypt

    e. God's promise, God's covenant

2. The first major division includes:

    a. Creation of heaven, earth, seas, animals, people

    b. Call of Abraham, Call of Isaac, Call of Jacob

    c. Call of Abraham, Promise of Canaan, Promise of Isaac

    d. Covenant with Noah, Covenant with Abraham and Sarah

    e. Creation, Disobedience, Flood and tower

3. The second major division of Genesis includes:

    a. Abraham, Sarah, and Isaac; Jacob; Joseph

    b. Birth of Moses, Call of Moses, Plagues

    c. First disobedience, First murder, Destruction of earth by flood

    d. Covenant with Israelites, Giving of the law

    e. Noah, Tower of Babylon, Abraham and Sarah, Isaac and Rebecca

4. The book of Genesis begins and concludes respectively with:

    a. Creation of universe, Death of Joseph

    b. Creation of sky and earth, Covenant with Noah

    c. Garden of Eden, Death of Jacob

    d. God's promise to Noah, Wandering in the desert

    e. Creation of people, First Passover

5. Exodus includes three major divisions:

    a. Rise to Power, Slavery and Passover, Law

    b. Call of Moses, Disasters, Disobedience

    c. Moses and the Exodus, Journey to Sinai, At Sinai

    d. Joseph, Disasters, Sea of Reeds

    e. Mt. Sinai, Sacred Tent, Conquest of Canaan

6. The first major division of Exodus includes:

    a. Famine, Food distribution, Leaving Egypt, Danger and rescue

    b. Birth of Moses, Flight to Midian, Burning bush

    c. Abraham, Isaac, Jacob

    d. Covenant, Ten Commandments, Moses' marriage

    e. Oppression, Call of Moses, Disasters, Deliverance

7. The last major division of Exodus includes:

    a. Covenant and law, Priestly law, Sacred Tent

    b. Building the golden calf, Punishment

    c. Panic at Sea of Reeds, Defeat for the Egyptians

    d. Covenant and Ten Commandments, Golden calf

    e. Entering Canaan, Siege of Jericho

8. Exodus begins and concludes respectively with:

    a. Dreams interpreted, Second stone tablets

    b. The new king, The cloud over the Tent

    c. Order to kill Hebrew baby boys, Israelites are freed

    d. Reaching Mt. Sinai, Israelites enter Jericho

    e. Abraham sets out, Sea closes over Egyptians

Sequence. Number events in EACH of the four groups in the order of their occurrence as recorded in Genesis and Exodus.

I. ____ There was day and night.

   ____ Isaac marries Rebecca.

   ____ People disobey for the first time.

   ____ People build the Tower of Babylon.

   ____ God calls Abraham.

   ____ Rainbow is sign of covenant.

II. ____ Jacob struggles with God.

   ____ Jacob settles in Egypt.

   ____ Esau sells his rights as oldest son.

   ____ Joseph administers food plan.

   ____ Jacob deceives Isaac.

   ____ Laban tricks Jacob.

III. ____ Israelites cross Sea of Reeds.

____ Moses accepts the Lord's call.

____ Frogs plague Egypt.

____ Egyptian king's daughter adopts Moses.

____ New Egyptian ruler fears Hebrews.

IV. ____ The Sacred Tent is erected.

____ Sacrifice offered at foot of Sinai.

____ The Lord gives the Ten Commandments.

____ The cloud settles on the Tent.

____ The Lord provides food in the desert.

B. NARRATIVE

Relationships. Beside EACH pair of names, write ONE symbol from these:

B = Brothers   SB = Sister, Brother   S = Sisters

HW = Husband, Wife   PC = Parent, Child

____Jacob, Joseph   ____Joseph, Benjamin

____Leah, Rachel   ____Noah, Shem

____Isaac, Esau   ____Jacob, Leah

____Sarah, Isaac   ____Miriam, Aaron

____Cain, Seth   ____Moses, Zipporah

Women. Identify EACH of the following women by writing the number of her name before the phrase with which she is MOST closely associated.

____Expelled from her home   1. Rachel

____Had son at age of 90   2. Hagar

____Condemned by mistress, saved by 3. Zipporah
God
                                     4. Eve
____Helped her son deceive his
father   5. Miriam

____Well-loved by husband   6. Dinah

____Vindicated by her brothers   7. Sarah

____Helped her brother be rescued   8. Rebecca

____Married a lawgiver   9. Leah

____Tricked Judah into giving her   10. Tamar
sons

____The substitute bride

Men. Identify EACH man by writing his number before the ONE term from the list opposite, with which he is most closely associated.

____Ashamed of his acts   1. Noah

____Built the first city   2. Abraham

____Escaped world destruction   3. Adam

____Believed God would keep His   4. Isaac
promise
                                     5. Cain
____Had twin sons

____Stole his brother's blessing   1. Aaron

____Saved people from starvation   2. Joseph

____Suggested that Moses delegate   3. Moses
authority
                                     4. Jacob
____Spoke to the king of Egypt for
his brother   5. Jethro

____Led the Israelites to freedom

____Sold his birthright   1. Simeon

____Blessed Abraham   2. Esau

____Slave's son whose life God   3. Lot
saved
                                     4. Melchizedek
____Held hostage for Benjamin
                                     5. Ishmael
____Escaped death at Sodom

Places. Identify the following places by writing the number of EACH place before the term with which it is most closely associated.

____God promised it to Hebrews.   1. Eden

____God renewed his covenant with   2. Ararat
Jacob.
                                     3. Ur
____Eliezer found Rebecca.
                                     4. Haran
____Evil city was destroyed.
                                     5. Canaan
____Noah arrived after the flood.
                                     6. Hebron
____First disobedience took place.
                                     7. Sodom
____Abraham buried Sarah near here.
                                     8. Bethel
____Abraham and family left their
home city.

____The Israelites agreed to obey   1. Egypt
the Lord.
                                     2. Marah
____Manna and quail were provided.
                                     3. Mt. Sinai
____Jacob settled here upon return
from Haran.   4. Sea of Reeds

____Hebrews were made slaves.   5. Desert of
                                         Sin
____Jacob wrestled with God.
                                     6. Peniel
____The Israelites walked across
to freedom.   7. Shechem

____Bitter water was made sweet.

C. FEATURES

Background. Circle the letter of the ONE BEST answer for each.

1. Genesis means
   a. General knowledge
   b. Oldest writing
   c. Religious account
   d. Beginning
   e. a and c

2. Genesis covers
   a. Creation to death of Joseph
   b. Flood to death of Joseph
   c. Creation to call of Abraham
   d. Creation to Exile
   e. Adam to Isaac

3. Exodus means
   a. The way out
   b. Covenant
   c. Departure from (Egypt)
   d. Law code
   e. a and c

4. Tradition holds that Genesis and Exodus were written by:
   a. Several writers
   b. Joshua
   c. J, E, D, and P
   d. Jacob, or Israel
   e. Moses

5. ALL of the following expressions reflect a modern consensus about the authorship of Genesis and Exodus EXCEPT:
   a. Written over a long period of time
   b. Product of a whole community of faith
   c. By Moses
   d. Anonymous
   e. 10th century to 5th century B.C.

Special content. Differentiate between these terms as true of Genesis or of Exodus, or found in that book, by writing G or E before each term.

____Seven years of famine

____The twelve sons of Jacob

____The twelve stones (pillars)

____The Ten Commandments

____Disasters (plagues)

____Jealous brothers

____"Let my people go."

____Covenant Box

____A king's dreams are interpreted.

____Sacred Tent

____Water from a rock

____"I will make you into a great nation."

____"You shall be my kingdom of priests."

____A father offers his son in sacrifice.

____"The Lord keep an eye on us..." (or "watch between you and me...")

Check answers on page 101. Compute your score on page 104 and enter on the growth record for Unit 2, page 106.

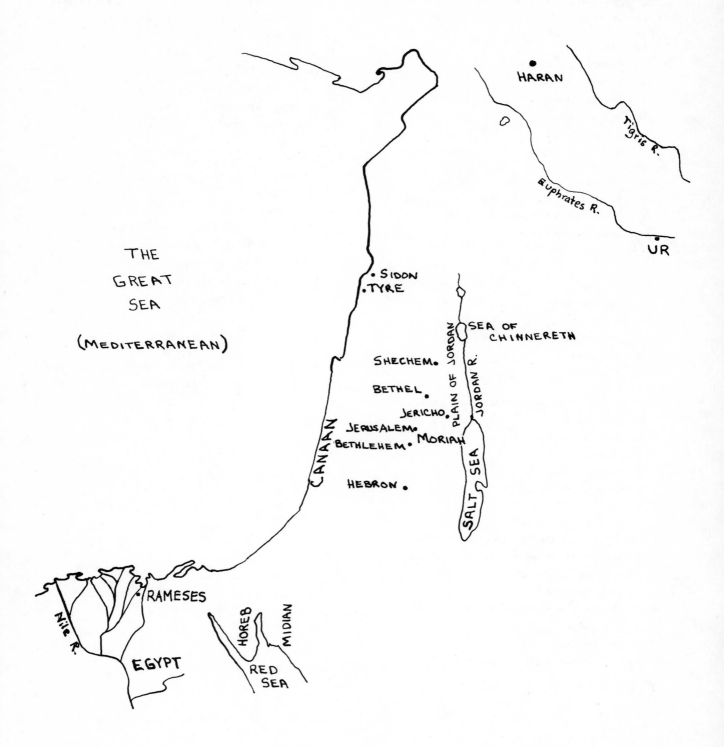

THE
GREAT
SEA

(MEDITERRANEAN)

HARAN

Tigris R.

Euphrates R.

UR

SIDON
TYRE

SEA OF
CHINNERETH

SHECHEM.

BETHEL.

JERICHO.

JERUSALEM.

BETHLEHEM.

MORIAH

HEBRON.

CANAAN

PLAIN OF JORDAN

JORDAN R.

SALT SEA

RAMESES

Nile R.

HOREB

MIDIAN

EGYPT

RED
SEA

INSTRUCTIONS

The questions which guide your reading of the Old Testament have been written on divided pages, so that you do not read down a page, but turn a page after reading only one portion. This probably seems strange to you, and at first may be awkward. However, you will soon find it very helpful. After thinking of your answers to the two or three questions, you turn the page to see the answers. If the questions went straight down the page, you would have to keep turning back and forth, because you could not remember so many answers at one time.

In Unit 2, Genesis and Exodus, the questions and answers which guide the reading of Genesis 1--25 appear in the top quarter of each page, numbered in the 100's. Those which guide the reading of Genesis 26--50 appear in the second quarter, numbered in the 200's. The questions for Exodus 1--15 appear in the third quarter and are numbered in the 300's. The guided reading for Exodus 16--40 appears in the bottom quarter, numbered in the 400's. You will read EACH quarter all the way through the unit before starting the next.

A reading assignment is given for each outline heading. To proceed:

1. Note the outline heading.
2. Read the questions about one book on one quarter-page to guide your reading.
3. Read the Bible passage assigned. When asked to scan a passage, you may skip it, or glance through it quickly, or read it. You will not be tested on it.
4. Reread the questions and then try to answer them from memory. (You need not write the answers unless this helps you.)
5. Look at the Bible to finish answering the questions.
6. Then and ONLY THEN turn the page to check your answers.
7. Note the drawings. They will help you remember the important points.
8. Periodically you will be referred to section charts which follow the divided pages. These section charts will add to your understanding of each book's structure, themes, and features throughout. Study the portion of the chart that covers the reading you have just completed.
9. Dividing the major section of each book, is a "Just for Fun" activity. If you do not find it fun, or do not have the time, you need not do the activity. These activities involve the application of facts you have been learning and sometimes the acquisition of more information by use of references.
10. Section tests follow the section charts. After completing the divided pages and section chart for Genesis 1--25, take Section Test 1. Upon checking your answers, return to page 41 to begin the study of Genesis 26--50. After completing Section Test 2, turn back to page 41 to begin the study of Exodus in Section 3. Using the same procedures, complete the study of Exodus in Section 4.
11. Upon completion of Section Test 4, begin Unit Test 2.
12. After checking your Unit Test answers and completing the Growth Record (growth in knowledge only), look up the references listed by any answers you missed. This will complete your mastery of basic content in Genesis and Exodus.

OUTLINES

GENESIS

110   PART 1:   THE BEGINNINGS OF HUMANITY   *(Chapters 1-11)*

    111   Creation of the Universe

    112   Disobedience and Disorder

    113   The Flood and the Tower of Babylon (Babel)

120   PART 2:   THE BEGINNINGS OF ISRAEL   *(Chapters 12-50)*

    121   TO CANAAN: ABRAHAM, SARAH, AND ISAAC   *(Chapters 12-25)*

        121A   The Call to Leave Home

        121B   The Covenant with Abraham

        121C   Isaac, the Promised Son

    222   IN CANAAN AND HARAN: JACOB   *(Chapters 25-36)*

        222A   Forced to Leave Canaan

        222B   Riches and Troubles in Haran

        222C   The Return to Canaan

    223   THE MOVE TO EGYPT: JOSEPH, THEN ISRAEL   *(Chapters 37-50)*

        223A   Dreams and Misfortunes

        223B   Joseph's Rise to Power

        223C   Reunion with Brothers

        223D   Israel's Move to Egypt

        223E   Deaths of Jacob and Joseph

EXODUS

310   EGYPT: MOSES AND THE EXODUS   *(Chapters 1-15)*

    311   Oppression: Call of Moses

    312   Disasters (Plagues)

    313   Deliverance: Passover and Exodus

420   DESERT: JOURNEY TO SINAI   *(Chapters 16-18)*

430   AT SINAI   *(Chapters 19-40)*

    431   Covenant and Law

    432   Priestly Laws: The Sacred Tent

100 INTRODUCTION TO GENESIS

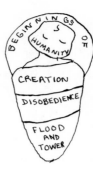

AUTHOR: Traditionally the entire Pentateuch has been ascribed to Moses, partly on the basis of a reference to his "writing the words of this law in a book, to the very end" (Deut. 31:24 RSV). Most scholars today understand this and similar verses to refer to limited portions within the Pentateuch, none of them in Genesis. On this view, the Pentateuch as a whole is anonymous (that is, the author is unnamed) and collective (that is, produced not by a single writer but by a whole community over a long period of time.)

DATE: If by Moses, about the 13th century B.C. If collective and anonymous, Genesis is the product of oral traditions from as early as the partriarchs incorporated into sources that were woven together in successive revisions from about the 10th to the 5th centuries B.C.

PURPOSE: To set forth Israel's historical traditions from creation to the death of Joseph in Egypt, thereby revealing a special understanding of God, of Israel, and of history.

FEATURES: Genesis (Greek for "beginning") takes it's name from the first words in the book, "In the beginning," as well as from the fact that its two major divisions tell of the beginnings of humanity (ch.1--11) and the beginnings of Israel (ch. 12--50). Although it contains a distinctive time pattern and a place pattern that moves from east to west across the Fertile Crescent, its basic pattern is one of persons, the ancestors of Israel, whose stories are linked by a series of genealogies.

Turn to 100 on next page.

****

300 INTRODUCTION TO EXODUS

AUTHOR AND DATE: The same as Genesis, whether Moses, ca. 13th century B.C. (traditional view), or collective and anonymous from 10th to 5th centuries B.C. (contemporary scholarship).

PURPOSE: To set forth Israel's historical traditions from slavery in Egypt to the establishment of the covenant at Sinai, and to incorporate in that history two great collections of Israel's law, the Decalogue (Ex. 20) and the Book of the Covenant (Ex. 21--23), and the beginning of a third, the Priestly Code (Ex. 25ff.).

FEATURES: (Greek for "the way out") takes it's name from the central event it tells about; the departure from Egypt. Although it is dominated by the personality of Moses, it's basic pattern is geographical. The first part of its story is set in Egypt (ch. 1--15), the second in the desert or wilderness (ch. 16--18), and the third at Sinai (ch. 19--40).

Turn to 300 on next page.

100 INTRODUCTION TO GENESIS

Circle the letters of ALL answers which apply. Then check with answers upside down above astericks.

1. Traditionally the author of Genesis has been viewed as:
    a. Abraham
    b. Moses
    c. Author of the whole Pentateuch
    d. Writing in about the 13th century B.C.
    e. Several different persons

2. According to most scholars today, Genesis is:
    a. Anonymous
    b. Collective
    c. The work of a single writer
    d. Dated in the time of Abraham
    e. Product of succesive revisions from 10th to 5th centuries B.C.

3. Genesis was written in order to:
    a. Record Israel's historical traditions
    b. Record Israel's laws
    c. Reveal how to build the Temple
    d. Reveal a special understanding of God, Israel, and history

4. Genesis means:
    a. Knowledge
    b. History
    c. Beginning
    d. Theology

1,bcd; 2,abe; 3,ad; 4,c

Go on to 110 on next page.

****

300 INTRODUCTION TO EXODUS

Circle the letters of ALL answers which apply.

1. Most scholars today believe the writer of Exodus was probably:
    a. One person
    b. More than one person
    c. Other than the writer of Genesis
    d. Moses

2. Exodus includes:
    a. Historical traditions
    b. Stories of the patriarchs
    c. Collections of Israel's law
    d. The Decalogue
    e. The Book of the Covenant

3. Exodus means:
    a. Settling in the Promised Land
    b. The way out
    c. Departure from Egypt
    d. Covenant

4. The dominant personality in Exodus is:
    a. Joseph
    b. Aaron
    c. Moses
    d. Miriam

5. Exodus is characterized by:
    a. A basic geographical pattern
    b. Division into two main parts
    c. Egypt/Desert/Sinai
    d. Moses/Aaron/Joshua

1,b; 2,acde; 3,bc; 4,c; 5,ac

Go on to 110 on next page.

GENESIS

110 Part I: THE BEGINNINGS OF HUMANITY (chapters I--II)

111 Creation of the Universe

Read Genesis 1 (to 2:4a)

In whose likeness did God fashion man and woman,
and over what did he tell them to rule?

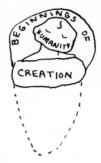

Turn to 111 on the next page.
****

222   IN CANAAN AND HARAN: JACOB (chapters 25--36)

222A Forced to Leave Canaan

Read Genesis 25:19--28:22.

1. When Rebecca finally became pregnant,
    how did the Lord explain her pain?
2. What did Esau swear to give Jacob as
    payment for the meal Jacob cooked?
3. What pair deceived Isaac, and why?

Turn to 222A on the next page.
****

EXODUS

310 EGYPT: MOSES AND THE EXODUS (chapters 1--15)

311 Oppression: Call of Moses (chapters 1--6)

Read Exodus 1:1--2:10.

1. As the new king saw the Hebrews
    increasing rapidly, he feared their
    gaining control of Egypt. What step
    did he take first?
2. Which two planned and worked so Moses could be saved?

3. Who adopted Moses?

Turn to 311 on the next page.
****

420 DESERT: JOURNEY TO SINAI

Read Exodus 16--18. (Start at 15:22.)

1. What happened when Moses threw the
    piece of wood (tree) in the water at Marah?
2. What did the Lord provide at Elim?

Turn to 420 on the next page.

111

Like himself, in his own image
The earth and every living thing

Go on to 112 on the next page.

****

222A

1. The <u>twins</u> she bore would become two nations and the elder
    serve the younger.
NOTE: Jacob (he takes by the heel) became Israel, while Esau
(covering, hair) is called Edom (red) = Edomites.
2. His rights as oldest son (birthright)
NOTE: The eldest Hebrew son inherited the largest share of
the family wealth and the right to rule the household.
NOTE also: God renewed his covenant with Isaac.
3. Rebecca and Jacob, to rob Esau of the blessing

Go on to 222A, next page.

****

311

1. He made the Hebrews work as slaves building the city of
    Ramses.
2. Moses' mother and sister Miriam
3. The king's (Pharaoh's) daughter
NOTE: "Pharaoh" is a title for the "king of Egypt" not the
name of a particular king.

Go on to 311, next page.

****

420

1. The bitter water became sweet.
2. Quails and manna
NOTE: "Manna" is a pun on "Man hu," Hebrew for "What is it?"

Go on to 420, next page.

42

112 Disobedience and Disorder (chapters 2--11)

Read Genesis 2--4 (from 2:4b). Scan 5 (skip, skim or read).

1. In the creation story, from which special tree did God
    forbid Adam and Eve to eat?

2. What are three results of disobedience mentioned in the
    story before the birth of the first child?

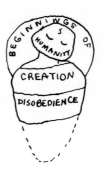

****

222A Forced to Leave Canaan *(continued)*

4. As Jacob fled for his life, what did God promise him at Bethel?

221B Riches and Troubles in Haran

Read Genesis 29--31.

NOTE: Haran was in Mesopotamia (=Paddan-Aram).

1. After working seven years for the bride he wanted, what
    happened on Jacob's wedding night?

2. What happened a week later?

3. Obeying a vision, Jacob left for Canaan without telling
    Laban. What happened at Mizpah (watch post)?

****

311 Oppression: Call of Moses

Read Exodus 2:11--6:23. Scan 6:14-27.

4. Who was Zipporah?

5. After attracting Moses' attention by the burning bush, what
    plan for Moses did the Lord describe?

****

420 DESERT: JOURNEY TO SINAI *(continued)*

3. What did Moses do for the people at Massah/Meribah?

112

1. The tree of knowledge of good and evil.
2. Any three of the following:

   Adam and Eve felt shame.
   The serpent crawled.
   Childbirth was painful for women.
   People had to work hard to live.
   Adam and Eve were expelled from Eden.

****

222A

4. God promised to bless him with many descendants and the land of Canaan.

222B

1. Laban tricked Jacob, giving him the older sister Leah instead of beautiful Rachel.
2. Laban also gave Rachel to Jacob for another seven years of labor.
3. Laban followed Jacob and said the pile of rocks (pillar) would be a sign that they would not harm each other. "The Lord watch between you and me, when we are absent one from the other." (Gen. 31:49 RSV)

****

311

4. Wife of Moses and daughter of Jethro (Reuel), the priest of Midian
5. To send Moses to the king and to bring the Israelites out of Egypt

****

420

3. He struck the rock with his staff and the Lord provided water from the rock.

112 Disobedience and Disorder *(continued)*

3. Who was the first murderer? First city builder?

4. Who was Adam's third son, and what happened when he, in turn, became a father?

****

JUST FOR FUN!

Find and identify the women of Genesis and the places in which they were active by underlining the letters which spell ONE NAME and ONE PLACE in EACH sentence. The following example identifies the book of the Bible and place: Example: Imo<u>gene</u>, <u>sis</u>ter of the bride, took charge of <u>the art here</u>.

1. Have you ever tried encouraging her?

2. Melissa raided the cooky jar in a hurry.

3. The agenda listed the S.A.R. ahead of Americana and research.

4. Aha! Garter snakes in the house. Let's hurry and catch them.

5. I had an earache last night so Martha ran over to help me.

(Answers on next page)
****

311 Oppression: Call of Moses *(continued)*

6. Back in Egypt, who went with Moses to ask the king for time to worship the Lord?

7. What did the king of Egypt do when asked to let the Israelites go?

8. What promise did the Lord renew with Moses?

****

420 DESERT: JOURNEY TO SINAI *(continued)*

4. At Rephidim Moses raised his arms and tried to keep them up. How did this help the Israelites?

5. What advice did Jethro give Moses?

3. Cain

4. Seth; people called upon the name of the Lord after
   his first son was born.

NOTE: Seth's descendants in Genesis 5 and Luke 3.

****

JUST FOR FUN!

1. Have you _ever_ _tried_ _en_couraging her?

2. Melis_sa_ _rai_ded the cooky jar in a _hurry_.

3. The agenda listed the _S.A.R._ _ah_ead of Ameri_cana_ _and_ research.

4. _Aha!_ _Gar_ter snakes in the house. Let'_s_ _hurry_ and catch them.

5. I had an e_arache_ _last_ night so Mar_tha_ _ran_ over to help me.

Another JUST FOR FUN!

Memorize the twelve sons of Jacob (=tribes of Israel) by mother
and age. Check yourself in Genesis 29:31--30:24 and 35:16-20.

****

6. Aaron

7. He forced the Hebrews to collect straw for the bricks while
   making the same quantity each day.

8. To be the God of Israel and to give Canaan to Israel.

********************** ******

4. It gave the Israelites victory over the Amalekites who had
   attacked them.

5. To appoint leaders to settle minor disputes and deal only
   with the harder questions himself.

JUST FOR FUN!

You may enjoy tracing the family line from Adam and Eve on through Abraham by drawing a family tree. Perhaps you would like to identify the different nationalities which developed along the line. Check passages listed on the next page.

****

222C The Return to Canaan

Read Genesis 32--36. Scan 36:1-5, 9-42.

1. Jacob's fear of Esau made him turn to God. What happened at Peniel?
2. In what city did Jacob settle?

NOTE: Jacob's sons killed and plundered Shechem because sister, Dinah, was raped by a Hivite.

****

JUST FOR FUN!

When the Lord called Moses to lead the Hebrews to freedom, Moses agreed that someone should do it, but not he! He gave reasons why he was a poor choice for the job (Ex. 3:11,13; 4:1,10).

Consider the injustices you have shaken your head over recently: problems in your church, your community, your nation. Perhaps your awareness of the injustice means God has something in mind for you to do. Give the problem some thought, analysis, and prayer. List in three columns: Problem; My Excuse; God's Answer. Then decide how to act.

****

JUST FOR FUN!

Fill in the blanks with place names that make puns in English:

When the Israelites had walked for three days in the desert without seeing anybody else, they said, "This place _____ is deserted!" They got mighty thirsty, and when they finally found water it was so bitter that they shuddered clear to the _____ of their bones. Moses sweetened the water, then they moved on and camped where there were twelve springs and seventy palm trees. That oasis had a name they remembered a few days later in another desert when they accused Moses of bringing them out to _____-inate them. The mean things they said about Moses in that desert were downright_____-ful. They were actually ready to kill Moses and sing "_____'s in de cold, cold ground."

JUST FOR FUN!

Check the following passages for Abraham's ancestors who started
different nationalities:

Genesis 4:1-2,25

Genesis 5:6,9,12,15,18,21,25,28-29,32

Genesis 10:1-31

Genesis 11:10-30

****

222C

1. At Peniel Jacob wrestled with God and had his name changed
    to Israel, meaning "he struggles (strives) with God."
2. Shechem in Canaan (via Succoth)

****

JUST FOR FUN!

See if you can learn in order the ten disasters (plagues) by
which God punished Egypt. After you've reviewed them in Exodus 7--11,
say them over from memory. Then check the answers below.

*Turn to page 61 and study the top portion of Section Chart 3. Then
continue guided reading on page 49.*

Answers: Blood, frogs, gnats, flies, death of animals, boils,
hail, locusts, darkness, death of the first-born.

****

JUST FOR FUN!

Answers: Shur   Marah   Elim   Sin   Massah

*Turn to page 62 and study the top portion of Section Chart 4. Then
continue guided reading on page 49.*

113 The Flood and the Tower of Babylon (=Babel)

Read Genesis 6--11. Scan 10 and 11:10-32.

1. When the ark landed on Ararat, to whom did God promise he would never again destroy all living beings? What was the sign of this covenant?

2. Where and how does Genesis say that God limited the people's pride after they built a city and tower?

****

221C The Return to Canaan *(continued)*

3. Where did God renew the covenant with Jacob?

4. Who was Jacob's youngest son, and what happened to the mother?

****

312 Disasters (Plagues)

Read Exodus 7--11 (starting at 6:28).

1. What did the Lord tell Moses would happen when he and Aaron spoke to the Pharaoh?

2. How did the Lord show his power?

****

430 AT SINAI (Exodus 19--40)

431 Covenant and Law (chapters 19--24)

Read Exodus 19--20. (Stop at 20:21.)

1. Where did the Israelites meet the Lord?

2. How did the Israelites answer when the Lord said they must keep the covenant?

113

1. Noah
   Rainbow
2. At the Tower of Babylon (Babel) God made people speak
   different lauguages so they could not understand each
   other.

Turn to page 59 and study the top portion of Section Chart 1.   Then
continue work on page 51.

****

222C

3. Bethel (meaning "house of God")
4. Benjamin
   Rachel died in childbirth.

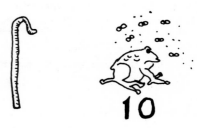

****

312

1. The Pharoah would be stubborn, but the Lord would free the
   Israelites.
2. By miracles through Aaron's walking stick, and by the ten
   disasters (plagues) on Egypt.

Turn to page 61 and study the middle portion of Section Chart 3.
Then continue guided reading on page 51.

****

431

1. At Mt. Sinai (Horeb), where God had first called Moses.
2. We will do whatever the Lord has said.

120 Part 2: THE BEGINNINGS OF ISRAEL (Genesis 12--50)

121 TO CANAAN: ABRAHAM, SARAH, AND ISAAC (chapters 12--25)

121A The Call to Leave Home

Read Genesis 12--14.

1. Abraham and Sarah left Ur for Haran. What did God command and what did he promise?

2. What did Melchizedek, priest and king of Salem, do?

************** *************

JUST FOR FUN!

Special names were given to the God of Abraham, of Isaac, and of Jacob. Do you recognize them from these symbols? Check Genesis 15:1; 31:42,53.

In the covenant with Noah, God was known as "Elohim," meaning "God." In the covenant with Abraham, God was known as "El Shaddai," meaning "God Almighty." What was the sign of this covenant? (See Gen. 17:11-12.)

********** *************** **

313 Deliverance: Passover and Exodus

Read Exodus 12--15 (Stop at 15:21.)

1. In what way was the Passover associated with the last plague?

2. What frightened the Israelites as they were leaving Egypt upon order of the king?

****

431 Covenant and Law *(continued)*

3. What major group of laws did the Lord give the Israelites?

Scan Exodus 21--23 (starting at 20:22).

Note matters treated.   Of special interest:
  21:23-25   23:2   23:14-17
  22:18   23:6-8
  22:26-27   23:9

Read Exodus 24.

4. To seal the covenant, sacrifice was offered on an altar near twelve stones (pillars) at the foot of the mountain, and seventy leaders ate before God on the mountain. Afterward, what did Moses do?

121A

1. To go to a land he would show him

    He promised to bless Abraham and make him into a great nation.

2. Blessed Abram

****

JUST FOR FUN!

Shield of Abraham, Fear of Isaac, Strong One (Mighty One) of Jacob

Circumcision

Turn to page 60 and study the top portion of Section Chart 2.
Then continue work on page 53.

****

313

1. Death struck the oldest son of each Egyptian family; but all
   Hebrews were saved by death passing over their homes while
   they ate the passover feast as commanded.
2. The king's chariots and soldiers chasing them.

****

431

3. The Ten Commandments (or Decalogue)
4. Moses went up the mountain for 40 days.

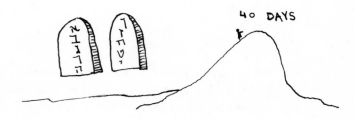

121B The Covenant with Abraham

Read Genesis 15--20.

1. In the vision, what did the Lord promise Abram?
2. What did Sarai do when they were old and still had no child?
3. To what promise did Abram's and Sarai's new names refer? What was the sign of the covenant?
4. Who were saved from the destruction of what town?

****

223 THE MOVE TO EGYPT: JOSEPH, THEN ISRAEL (chapters 37--50)

223A Dreams and Misfortunes

Read Genesis 37--39.

How did Joseph's brothers get back at Joseph for telling tales?

NOTE the contrast in Genesis 38 and 39: Tamar seduced Judah and got the sons he had wrongfully denied her. Her son Perez is in Jesus' genealogy.*(Continued on next page.)*

223 B Joseph's Rise to Power

Read Genesis 40--41.

1. How did Joseph interpret the king's dream?
2. What did the king of Egypt do for Joseph?

****

313 Deliverance: Passover and Exodus *(continued)*

3. How were the Israelites saved at the Sea of Reeds (Red Sea)?

****

432 Priestly Laws: The Sacred Tent (chapters 25--40)

Scan Exodus 25--31.(Note subject of each paragraph.)
Read Exodus 32--34.(Note that this completes the covenant narrative.)

1. Afraid when Moses did not return, what did the people want to make them feel safe?
2. How did the Israelites break the covenant?

121B

1. Abraham's own son and countless descendants
2. Sarai gave Hagar to Abram so he could have a child by Hagar.
3. Many descendants: the land of Canaan: Abraham means "Father of
   a multitude." Sarah means "Princess" (mother of kings and nations)
   Sign: circumcision
4. Lot and his two daughters from Sodom

****

223A They sold him into slavery.

NOTE (continued): Potiphar's wife failed to seduce Joseph, who was
      vindicated by advancement, though her lie put him in prison first.

223B

1. There would be seven years of plenty and seven years of famine.
2. Put him in control of Egypt to administer the food storage and
   distribution. He also gave Joseph a wife.
NOTE: During the years of plenty, Joseph had two sons, Manasseh
      and Ephraim.

****

313

3. A strong east wind drove the waters back so the Israelites could
   cross. The Egyptian chariots got stuck; Egyptians panicked and
   were covered by returning waters.

****

432

1. A god to go ahead of them
2. By bowing and sacrificing before the golden calf Aaron made

121C Isaac, the Promised Son

  Read Genesis 21--24. Scan 25:1-6, 12-18. Read 25:7-11.

1. What was unusual about the birth of Isaac? (See also 17:17.)
2. How did God bless Ishmael and Hagar?
3. God tested Abraham's faith by asking him to sacrifice Isaac.
    When Isaac was spared, what did Abraham call the place?
4. Abraham purchased his first land in Canaan for Sarah's grave
    at Hebron. Who brought Rebecca to Isaac, and why was she
    considered appropriate?

                    ****

223C Reunion with Brothers

  Read Genesis 42--45.

1. How did Joseph happen to see ten of his brothers?
2. How did Joseph reassure his brothers that he had forgiven them?

223D Israel's Move to Egypt

  Read Genesis 46--47 (to 47:26). Scan 46:8-25.

1. What did God tell Jacob at Beersheba?
2. Where was the land that Pharaoh gave to Jacob and his household?

                    ****

313   Deliverance: Passover and Exodus *(continued)*

4. A psalm closes this first act of the drama. Who sang it and
    why?

                    *************************** **

432   Priestly Laws   *(continued)*

3. When the Lord renewed the covenant, what great thing did he
    promise to do for the Israelites?

    Scan Exodus 35--39 (note it echoes 25--31). Read Exodus 40.

4. After the Tent of the Lord's presence was erected, furnished,
    and consecrated, what happened to the cloud?

121C

1. Both parents were very old.
   (Abraham 100, Sarah 90)
2. God provided water to save their lives and promised to make Ishmael
   father of a great nation. (Ishmaelites=Bedouins)
3. "The Lord provides."
4. Abraham's oldest servant (Eliezer, Genesis 15:2)
   Because she was a relative, the daughter of Abraham's nephew.

****

223C

1. All but Benjamin had come to Egypt to buy grain during the
   famine.
2. He told them it was God's plan so he could save the family
   from starving.

223D

1. God said that he would make a great nation of Jacob in Egypt;
   that he would go with him into Egypt and bring him out again.
NOTE that 70 persons came into Egypt as Jacob's household.
2. Goshen (the best part of the land).

****

313

4. First, Moses and the people sang to praise God for freeing
   them. Then Miriam led the women dancing and singing the first
   lines as a refrain.

****

432

3. To drive out all the other people from the land which he
   promised to the Israelites.
4. It settled over the Tent.

JUST FOR FUN!

Locate some of the places listed below on the map (page 36) and then draw them on the outline map on page 71. You can trace the ground that Abraham covered in his lifetime.

Ur   Egypt   Hebron

Haran   Bethel   Moriah

Shechem   Plain of Jordan

****

223E Deaths of Jacob and Joseph

Read Genesis 47--50 (from 47:27).

1. Joseph swore to Jacob that he would bury him in Canaan. How did Jacob bless the house of Joseph?
2. Which two of Jacob's sons received the longest blessings from him?
3. Where did Joseph and his brothers bury Jacob?
4. How did Joseph answer when his brothers begged forgiveness?

NOTE: Joseph made all the sons of Israel swear that they would take his bones back to Canaan.

****

JUST FOR FUN!

Several places have been mentioned in this first part of Exodus. Using the map on page 36 for reference, place the following names in the correct location on the map on page 71 and tell what happened at each in Exodus 1--15.

Rameses   Nile River   Midian   Horeb   Canaan

****

JUST FOR FUN!

Looking back at the whole book of Exodus, we see it has three main parts, with a dramatic climax at the end of Part 1: the Exodus event. Just for fun, you might like to re-read Exodus 15:1-21 and see how the literary type of that passage sets the flavor and underscores the meaning of the whole first part of the book. Is it prose or poetry? Like what precedes and follows it, or different? What <u>kind</u> of prose or poetry is it? Look at the verse that is repeated, 15:1 and 21. What would be the <u>occasion</u> for a verse like this? Now look at 15:2-18. On what occasion or in what place would people sing words like these? (Think first, then see next page.)

JUST FOR FUN!

Perhaps you would like to draw symbols for the different events: a throne for the visit to the king of Egypt, a tree for the visit by the three strangers, flames for Sodom, a well at Haran, etc. The outline map can be a pictorial one.

Turn to page 59 and study Section Chart 1.   Then take Section Test 1.

****

223E

1. By blessing Ephraim and Manasseh, Joseph's sons (Ephraim as the greater)

2. Judah and Joseph

NOTE: The tribe of Judah later formed the bulk of the Southern Kingdom; the tribes of Ephraim and Manasseh (House of Joseph) became the core of the Northern Kingdom.

3. In the cave near Mamre (Hebron) where Sarah, Abraham, Isaac, and Rebecca were buried.

4. By telling them, "Fear not....You meant evil against me; but God meant it for good...." (Gen. 50:19-20 RSV)

Turn to page 60 and study Section Chart 2.   Then take Section Test 2.

****

JUST FOR FUN!

Rameses	Store city built by king of Egypt using Hebrew slaves
Nile River	Where Moses as a baby was found by the king's daughter
Midian	Where Moses fled after killing Egyptian, and stayed until called
Horeb	"Mountain of God" where Moses received call, also called Sinai
Canaan	The promised land where Moses was leading the Israelites

Study Section Chart 3 on page 61.   Then take Section Test 3.

****

JUST FOR FUN!

Millions of people, Jews and Christians, know the Ten Commandments by heart. Care to join the club? See Exodus 20:2-17.

Answers to preceding JUST FOR FUN: Poetry; different. A <u>song</u> of praise; 15:1,21 is a <u>victory</u> song sung after battle; 15:2-18 is a hymn of praise, sung in corporate worship.

Study Section Chart 4 on page 62.   Then take Section Test 4.

SECTION CHART I: GENESIS

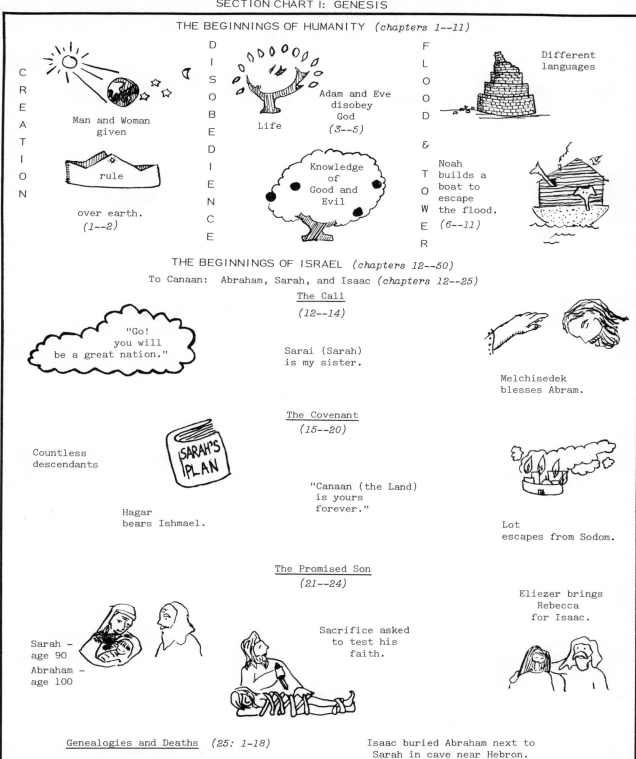

THE BEGINNINGS OF HUMANITY *(chapters 1--11)*

C R E A T I O N

Man and Woman given

rule

over earth.
(1--2)

D I S O B E D I E N C E

Life

Adam and Eve disobey God
(3--5)

Knowledge of Good and Evil

F L O O D & T O W E R

Different languages

Noah builds a boat to escape the flood.
(6--11)

THE BEGINNINGS OF ISRAEL *(chapters 12--50)*

To Canaan: Abraham, Sarah, and Isaac *(chapters 12--25)*

The Call
(12--14)

"Go! you will be a great nation."

Sarai (Sarah) is my sister.

Melchisedek blesses Abram.

The Covenant
(15--20)

Countless descendants

SARAH'S PLAN

Hagar bears Ishmael.

"Canaan (the Land) is yours forever."

Lot escapes from Sodom.

The Promised Son
(21--24)

Sarah - age 90
Abraham - age 100

Sacrifice asked to test his faith.

Eliezer brings Rebecca for Isaac.

__Genealogies and Deaths__ *(25: 1-18)*

Isaac buried Abraham next to Sarah in cave near Hebron.

(After studying the chart, take Section Test 1 on page 63.)

THE BEGINNINGS OF ISRAEL *(chapters 12--50, continued)*

In Canaan and Haran: Jacob *(chapters 25--36)*

Forced to Leave
Canaan
(25:19--28:22)

Bartered: Birthright
Stolen: Blessing

At Bethel:

"I'll bless you
and give you
Canaan (the Land)."

Riches and
Troubles in
Haran
(29--31)

Older sister--
substitute bride,
Leah

Beautiful younger
sister, Rachel

"The Lord watch
between you and me."

Return
to Canaan

(32--36)

The name Israel
means striving
with God.

"Nations and
kings from you"

Esau
forgives
Jacob

The Move to Egypt: Joseph, Then Israel *(chapters 37--50)*

Dreams and
Misfortunes
(37--39)

The dreamer

DISLIKED by
his brothers

Sold as a
slave
into Egypt

Rise to
Power
40--41

Joseph warned of
famine

Reunion
(42--45)

Brothers bow, but
Benjamin
stayed home with
Jacob.

Israel
Moves

(46:1--47:26) "I will make a
great nation

of you in Egypt."

Deaths
(47:27--50:26)

Joseph says,
"It was God's
plan.

"You meant evil
against me.

"God meant it for good."

After studying the chart, take Section Test 2 on page 65.

EGYPT: MOSES AND THE EXODUS *(chapters 1--15)*

Oppression: Call of Moses *(chapters 1--6)*

Moses kills an Egyptian
and flees to Midian.

Aaron
and Moses:
"Let my people
go worship!"

Hebrews are
made slaves.

The Lord (God)
calls Moses.

Miriam watches baby in
basket.

King: "No! And they
shall find their
own straw
to make
bricks."

Genealogies *(6:15--27)*

Disasters *(chapters 7--11)*

"I will show my
power and free
my people so the
Egyptians will
know I am the Lord."

Signs of the Lord's
power through Aaron's
walking stick (rod)

The Lord sends disasters
(plagues) on the Egyptians.

Deliverance: Passover and Exodus *(chapters 12--15)*

Hebrews   Egyptians

The Passover

"We'd rather be slaves."

Sing to the Lord!

Crossing the Sea of
Reeds (Red Sea)

A strong east wind.

The horse and his
rider

hurled into the
sea

Miriam leads the

women in praise.

After studying the chart, take Section Test 3 on page 67.

DESERT: JOURNEY TO SINAI *(chapters 16--18)*

God Helps Israelites:

| Marah | Desert of Sin | Rephidim | Massah/Meribah |

Bitter
water

Manna and quails

Israelites
defeat
Amalekites

Water
from rock

Israelites Help Moses:

Reunion

Jethro brings
Zipporah to Moses.

Jethro's good advice

Appoint leaders to
settle the small disputes.

AT SINAI *(chapters 19--40)*

Covenant and Law *(19--24)*

The Lord:
"Keep my
covenant (commandments)."

The Israelites:
"We will obey."

Covenant Sealed

Mt. Sinai

Moses stays
40 days.

Priestly Laws: The
Sacred Tent
(chapters 25--40)

Instructions
for Tent and
furnishings
(25--31)

"People bow (worship) and sacrifice
before the calf Aaron made.

Cloud settles
over the Tent.

After studying the chart, take Section Test 4 on page 68.

A. STRUCTURE

Outline. Review headings 110 - 121C on **page 38**, study structure of Section Chart 1, then complete the following outline of Genesis 1--25.

Part 1 (1) THE BEGINNINGS OF _____
    I.(2) _____ of the Universe
   II.(3) _____ and Disorder
  III.(4) The _____ and the _____
        of Babylon (Babel).

Part 2 (5) THE _____ OF _____
    I.(6) TO_____:_____,
        SARAH, AND ISAAC
      A. (7) The _____ to Leave Home
      B. (8) The _____ with Abraham
      C. (9) Isaac, the _____

Sequence. Number the following events in order as they occur in Genesis.

_____ A flood covers the earth.
_____ Rebecca marries Isaac.
_____ Lot escapes the destruction of Sodom.
_____ God gives people rule over all living things.
_____ God calls Abraham.
_____ A baby is born to an elderly couple.

B. NARRATIVE

Happenings. Circle the ONE BEST answer.
1. The first disobedience mentioned in Genesis resulted in ALL of the following EXCEPT:
   a. A feeling of shame
   b. People hating serpents
   c. Painful childbirth
   d. Illness from eating a certain fruit
   e. Hard labor in order to survive

2. God made people speak in different languages at the Tower of Babel because of ALL of the following EXCEPT:
   a. He didn't like the language they were speaking.
   b. He didn't want them to understand each other.
   c. They had tried to build a tower that reached to the heavens.
   d. They had built a city.
   e. He wanted to limit their pride.

3. When Abraham and Sarah were very old and still had no children:
   a. God told them they would have children through adoption.
   b. They thought they could still have a son through Sarah's slave.
   c. They knew God would send them many children in their old age.
   d. Hagar had a son who became father of the Bedouins.
   e. b and d

4. ALL of the following are recorded in Genesis concerning God's covenant with Abraham EXCEPT that:
   a. He promised Abraham and Sarah the land of Canaan.
   b. He said their son would become a great ruler.
   c. He changed their names to Abraham and Sarah.
   d. He required the sign of circumcision of Abraham's household and descendants.

Places. Identify the place where each event took place by writing the number of EACH place before the ONE event with which it is most closely associated.

_____Eliezer found Rebecca.   1.   Eden

_____Lot escaped its destruction.   2.   Ararat

_____Land was promised to Abraham's descendants.   3.   Ur

_____God brought Sarah, Abraham, and his father   4.   Haran
            out of the city.   5.   Babylon (Babel)

_____Abraham bought a cave for Sarah's tomb.   6.   Canaan

_____The ark rested after the flood.   7.   Salem

_____Melchizedek was king.   8.   Sodom

_____People first disobeyed.   9.   Hebron

_____People couldn't understand each other.   10.   "The Lord provides"

_____Abraham offered Isaac on an altar.

Relationships. Write the name of each woman's mate and of her son (if studied in Part 1) in the correct blank beside her name. Write only ONE name in EACH blank.

Woman	Mate	Son		Men	
Eve	_____	_____		Isaac	(Use twice)
Sarah	_____	_____		Abraham	(Use twice)
Hagar	_____	_____		Adam	(Use once)
Rebecca	_____	_____		Ishmael	(Use once)
				Seth	(Use once)

Women. Identify EACH woman by writing her number before the ONE term with which she is most closely associated.

_____Had son in old age.   1.   Hagar

_____Tested God's command.   2.   Sarah (Use twice)

_____Laughed on two important occasions.   3.   Eve

_____Blessed by God when mistreated by mistress.   4.   Rebecca

_____Bride from Haran.

Men. Identify EACH man by writing his number before the ONE term with which he is most closely associated.

_____Was the first man to disobey God.   1.   Noah

_____Killed his brother and built a city.   2.   Eliezer

_____Saved from the flood.   3.   Lot

_____Passed God's test of faith.   4.   Isaac

_____Abraham's nephew who chose the better land.   5.   Adam

_____A priest and king who blessed Abraham.   6.   Cain

_____Found a wife for Isaac.   7.   Ishmael

_____Saved from death and made father of the   8.   Abraham
            Bedouins.   9.   Melchizedek

_____Born in answer to a promise.

Check answers on page 101. Compute your score on page 104 and enter on the growth record for Unit 2 on page 106. After studying any items missed, continue with guided reading on page 41.

A. STRUCTURE

<u>Outline</u>. Review headings 22I – 222E, study Section Chart 2, then complete the following outline of Genesis 25--50.

Part 2 THE BEGINNINGS OF ISRAEL
    I. TO CANAAN: ABRAHAM, SARAH, AND ISAAC
   II. (1) IN CANAAN AND _____: _____
      A. (2) Forced to _____Canaan
      B. (3) _____and _____in Haran
      C. (4) The Return to _____
  III. (5) THE MOVE TO _____:_____,
        THEN ISRAEL
      A. (6) _____and Misfortunes
      B. (7) _____to Power
      C. (8) Reunion with _____
      D. (9) _____to Egypt
      E.(10) Deaths of Jacob and _____

<u>Sequence</u>. Number the following events in order as they occur in Genesis.

___A Hebrew makes Egypt more powerful.
___A brother is cheated.
___A woman dies in childbirth.
___Twins are born.
___A Hebrew works for his uncle in Haran.

B. NARRATIVE

<u>Happenings</u>. Circle the ONE BEST answer.

1. Because Rebecca helped Jacob deceive Isaac, ALL of the following are true EXCEPT:
   a. Esau was robbed of his blessing as oldest son.
   b. Esau planned to kill Jacob.
   c. Isaac punished Rebecca and Jacob.
   d. Isaac sent Jacob to Haran to get a wife.
   e. Jacob fled to Paddam-Aram (Haran, Mesopotamia) in fear and poverty.

2. After being tricked into another seven years of work to earn Rachel,
   a. Laban refused to let Rachel marry Jacob.
   b. Rachel refused to go with Jacob.
   c. Leah died.
   d. Jacob decided he didn't want Rachel.
   e. Jacob left for Haran without telling Laban.

3. Joseph told his father tales about his older brothers. They resented this and did ALL of the following EXCEPT:
   a. Planned to kill him.
   b. Stripped him of his clothes.
   c. Threw him in a pit.
   d. Put a lion in the pit.
   e. Sold him as a slave.

4. When Joseph's brothers came to buy grain, Joseph tested their sincerity and regard for their father in ALL these ways EXCEPT:
   a. He put money in their sacks which they returned.
   b. He kept Simeon hostage until they brought Benjamin.
   c. He said Benjamin would be his slave until Judah begged to take Benjamin's place.
   d. He put his cup in Benjamin's sack and then had it discovered.
   e. He kept Judah as slave until Jacob arrived.

5. When Joseph's brothers begged forgiveness for selling Joseph, he said:
   a. Their evil had made them all suffer.
   b. They should prove their sincerity by working for him.
   c. He had been at fault too.
   d. The family and many others were alive because he had come to Egypt.
   e. He was grateful to them because now he was in a position of power.

Places. Identify EACH place by writing the number of the place before the ONE happening with which
it is most closely associated.

_____Joseph and his brothers quarreled here.

1. Haran (Paddan-Aram)

_____"The Lord watch between you and me."

2. Bethel

_____Joseph rose to power.

3. Mizpah

_____Egyptian king gave this land to Israel.

4. Peniel

_____Rachel grew up here.

5. Shechem

_____Jacob struggled with God.

6. Egypt

_____God renewed his covenant with Jacob.

7. Beersheba

_____God told Jacob he would bring Israel back out of Egypt.

8. Goshen

Relationships. Write the name of EACH woman's mate and of her son in the correct blank beside
her name.   Write only ONE name in each blank.

Woman	Mate	Son
Rebecca	_____	_____
Rachel	_____	_____
Leah	_____	_____
Tamar	_____	_____

Isaac   (Use once)

Jacob   (Use more than once)

Judah   (Use more than once)

Joseph   (Use once)

Perez   (Use once)

Women. Identify each woman by writing the number of her name before the ONE term with which
she is most closely associated.

_____The bride who was substituted for her sister

1. Rebecca

_____Successfully obtained her rights from Judah

2. Rachel

_____Died when giving birth to Benjamin

3. Leah

_____Helped Jacob deceive Isaac

4. Dinah

_____Raped by a Hivite prince and revenged by her brothers

5. Tamar

Men. Identify EACH man by writing the number of his name before the ONE term with which he
is most closely associated.

_____Interpreted dreams

1. Jacob

_____House of Joseph who became the core of the Northern Kingdom

2. Esau

_____Descendants of Abraham who bought Joseph

3. Laban

_____Tricked Jacob

4. Joseph

_____Cheated his brother

5. Judah

_____Blessed the younger son by mistake

6. King of Egypt

_____Sold his birthright

7. Ishmaelites

_____Made Joseph second to him in power

8. Isaac

_____Offered to take Benjamin's place as slave

9. Ephraim and Manasseh

*Check answers on page 101.   Compute your score on page 104 and enter on the growth record for Unit 2
on page 106.   Study any items missed, and then begin the study of Exodus on page 41.*

A. STRUCTURE

Outline. Review headings 311A-C and Section Chart 2, then complete the following outline of the first 15 chapters of Exodus.

I. (1) _____ : MOSES AND THE _____

  A. (2) Oppression: _____ of _____

  B. (3) _____

  C. (4) _____ : _____ and Exodus

Sequence. Number the following events in order of their occurrence in Exodus.

___ The Lord tells Moses to free the Hebrew slaves.
___ Chariots get stuck, Egyptians panic at the
    Sea of Reeds.
___ The Pharaoh's daughter adopts a Hebrew baby.
___ Death passes over each Hebrew home, but strikes
    each Egyptian home.
___ The Hebrews are forced to do heavy labor under
    cruel conditions.
___ The Egyptians suffer disasters of sickness,
    storms, insects, etc.

B. NARRATIVE

Happenings. Circle the letter of the ONE BEST answer for each item.

1. The Hebrews had to work as slaves in Egypt for all these reasons EXCEPT:

  a. A new king came to the throne of Egypt.
  b. The Hebrews were making attacks on outlying
     towns.
  c. They were strong, healthy and increasing in
     number.
  d. The Pharaoh was afraid they might control
     Egypt.
  e. The new king did not like the Hebrews.

2. A burning bush on Mount Horeb

  a. Attracted Moses' attention
  b. Destroyed the vegetation there
  c. Appeared as a sign that the Lord would
     free the Israelites
  d. Appeared as a sign to the Egyptians of
     the Lord's power
  e. a and c

3. When Aaron and Moses asked Pharaoh to let the Hebrews go to worship the Lord, the King of Egypt

  a. Increased the work load of the Hebrews
  b. Let the Hebrews go
  c. Put Moses and Aaron in prison
  d. Ordered the Hebrew boy babies to be killed
  e. a and c

4. The Lord told Moses that when the King of Egypt became stubborn, the Lord would do ALL of the following EXCEPT:

  a. Assert his power
  b. Free the Israelites
  c. Show the Egyptians he was the Lord
  d. Remove Pharaoh from his throne
  e. Work against the Egyptians

5. The first Passover was

  a. Death passing over the Hebrew homes,
     leaving them safe
  b. Death striking the eldest son in each
     Egyptian family
  c. The Israelites passing over the Red Sea
  d. The feast and worship of the Israelites
     before leaving Egypt
  e. a and d

Persons. Identify the following persons by writing the number of EACH person's name before the ONE term with which it is most closely associated.

___ Watched over Moses at
    river's edge
___ Married Moses and bore him
    two sons
___ Enslaved the Hebrews
___ A priest who was Zipporah's
    father
___ Appointed spokesman for his
    brother
___ Heard and obeyed the Lord's
    command
___ Gave Moses an education
___ Planned a way for Moses to
    be rescued

1. King of Egypt
2. Mother of Moses
3. Moses
4. Miriam
5. Pharaoh's
   daughter
6. Jethro (Reuel)
7. Zipporah
8. Aaron

Places. Write the number of EACH place before ONE or MORE terms with which it is correctly associated.

___ The Lord told Moses to free
    the Israelites.
___ A new king enslaved the
    Israelites.
___ The Israelites were fright-
    ened by the appearance of
    Egyptian soldiers.
___ Moses received a good education.
___ Zipporah married Moses.
___ City built by Hebrew slaves.
___ Pharaoh's daughter found Moses.
___ A bush appeared on fire
    without burning.
___ Israelites walked across
    safely.
___ Moses fled here after killing
    a man.

1. Egypt
2. Rameses
3. Nile River
4. Midian
5. Mt. Horeb
6. Sea of Reeds
   (Red Sea)

Check answers on page 101. Compute your score on page 104 and enter on the growth record for Unit 2 on page 106. After studying any items missed, continue with guided reading on page 41.

A. STRUCTURE

Outline. Review headings 4II-4I2B and Section Chart 4, then complete the following outline of Exodus 16--40.

II. (1) _____: JOURNEY TO _____

III. (2) AT_____

    A. (3) _____and_____

    B. (4) _____Laws: The Sacred_____

Sequence: Number the following events in order of their occurrence in Exodus.

___Jethro gives Moses good advice.
___Moses' staff brings water from the rock.
___A covenant is made with the Israelites.
___Raised arms bring victory over Amalekites.
___Bitter water is made sweet.
___The Tent of the Lord's presence is erected.
___Manna and quails are provided as food.
___Aaron makes a golden calf.
___Altar and twelve stones are set up.
___The Lord promised to drive out all other peoples
    from Canaan.
___Seventy leaders had a feast.

B. NARRATIVE

Happenings. Circle the letter of the ONE BEST answer for each item.

1. ALL of the following happened on the journey to Sinai EXCEPT:

    a. A rock was hit and water came out.
    b. The rod of the Lord was taken by the Amalekites.
    c. Sweet food was gathered each morning.
    d. Moses threw a piece of wood in the water.
    e. Aaron held up Moses' arms to win the battle.

2. When the Lord asked the Israelites to obey him, they accepted the covenant in ALL of the following ways EXCEPT:

    a. Saying they would do whatever the Lord said
    b. Building an altar at the foot of the mountain
    c. Building an altar at the top of the mountain
    d. Setting up twelve stones (pillars)
    e. Offering sacrifices at the altar

3. The Lord became very angry with the Israelites because they

    a. Came up the mountain
    b. Refused to accept Moses as their leader any longer
    c. Had a wild party to celebrate the covenant
    d. Broke the covenant
    e. Tried to return to Egypt

4. When Moses wrote on the second tablets, the Lord promised

    a. To drive all other peoples out of Canaan
    b. To make many great nations out of the Israelites
    c. To give the Israelites extra strength so they could get land
    d. They would never be in want again
    e. They would become the ancestors of a king who would rule forever

5. After the sacred Tent was erected and furnished, the Israelites would stay in camp each day until:

    a. They heard the voice of the Lord telling them to go.
    b. They had gathered all the manna.
    c. They had offered sacrifices to the Lord at the altar.
    d. The cloud covered the covenant Tent.
    e. The cloud left the Tent.

Persons. Write the number of EACH person before the ONE term with which it is most closely associated, but use ONE name TWO times.

___Built the gold bull (golden calf)
___Joined her husband at Rephidim
___Offered sacrifices as a sign
    the Israelites accepted the
    covenant
___Met the Lord at Mt. Sinai
___Told Moses to appoint leaders
    and delegate authority
___Wrote the Decalogue for the
    people

1. Moses (twice)
2. Jethro
3. Zipporah
4. Aaron
5. Israelites

Places. Write the number of EACH place before the ONE term with which it is most closely associated. Use ONE place TWO times.

___Bitter water was made sweet.
___The covenant was made.
___The Amalekites were defeated.
___The people questioned Moses'
    leadership because they had
    no water.
___Twelve stones were set up.
___The Israelites had water and
    food before the Desert of
    Sin.
___Manna and quail were provided
    each day.

1. Mt. Sinai (Horeb)
2. Elim
3. Desert of Sin
4. Rephidim
5. Marah
6. Masseh/ Meribah

Check answers on page 102. Compute your scores on page 104 and enter on the growth record for Unit 2 on page 106. After studying any missed answers and reviewing outlines and the section charts, take Unit Test 2 on the next page.

A. STRUCTURE

Outline. Complete the following outlines of Genesis and Exodus.

Genesis:
   I. THE (1) _____ OF _____
      A. (2) _____ of the Universe
      B. (3) _____ and Disorder
      C. (4) The _____ and the _____
         of _____
   II. THE (5) _____ OF _____
      A. (6) TO _____: _____, SARAH,
         AND ISAAC
      B. (7) IN CANAAN AND _____: _____
      C. (8) THE MOVE TO _____: _____,
         THEN ISRAEL

Exodus:
   I. (1) EGYPT: _____ AND THE _____
      A. (2) _____: _____ of Moses
      B. Disasters
      C. (3) Deliverance: _____ and _____
   II. (4) _____: JOURNEY TO _____
   III. (5) AT _____
      A. (6) _____ and _____
      B. (7) _____ Laws: the Sacred _____

Sequence. Number the following events in EACH group in the order in which they occur in Genesis and Exodus.

   I.

____ Abraham and Sarah have a son in their old age.
____ Jacob struggles with God.
____ Cain kills his brother, Abel.
____ Laban substitutes Leah as bride.
____ A rainbow is sign of God's covenant.

   II.

____ Joseph heads a food distribution program in Egypt.
____ Israelites experience first Passover.
____ Moses accepts his mission.
____ Joseph's brothers sell him.
____ A slave's baby is raised in palace.

   III.

____ Manna and quails are provided.
____ Leaders have a feast at Sinai.
____ A golden calf is built.
____ Ten Commandments are given.
____ Egyptian chariots get stuck.

B. NARRATIVE

Relationships. Write the name of each woman's mate and child in the blanks next to her name.

Woman	Mate	Child	
1. Eve	_____	_____	Judah (Use two times)
2. Sarah	_____	_____	Seth
3. Hagar	_____	_____	Perez
4. Rebecca	_____	_____	Moses
5. Rachel	_____	_____	Isaac (Use two times)
6. Leah	_____	_____	Joseph
7. Tamar	_____	_____	Abraham (Use two times)
8. Zipporah	_____	Gershom	Adam
			Ishmael
			Jacob
			(Use three times)

Men: Their Roles and Acts. Write the number of EACH man's name in the blank before the ONE phrase with which he is most closely associated.

____ Escaped Sodom's destruction
____ Obeyed God's call to leave home   1. Adam
____ Was offered as a sacrifice   2. Cain
____ Wanted to be equal with God   3. Noah
____ Given rainbow as sign of God's   4. Abraham
   promise   5. Lot
____ Saved from thirst to become   6. Melchizedek
   father of princes   7. Ishmael
____ Blessed Abraham   8. Isaac
____ Killed his brother and built
   first city

____ A priest who helped his brother
____ Tricked his nephew   1. Esau
____ A strong ruler in Egypt   2. Jacob
____ Israel   3. Laban
____ Advised a more efficient way   4. Judah
____ Offered to be a slave in place   5. Joseph
   of Benjamin   6. Moses
____ Doubted he could free the   7. Jethro
   Hebrews   8. Aaron
____ Forgave his brother

Women: Their Roles and Acts. Write the number of EACH woman's name in the blank before the ONE phrase with which she is most closely associated.

____ Took her sister's place as bride
____ Tricked Judah into giving her her
   rights   1. Miriam
____ God called her "mother of nations   2. Rebecca
   and kings"   3. Hagar
____ Had twelve brothers   4. Rachel
____ Encouraged her son to deceive his   5. Sarah
   father   6. Zipporah
____ Disobeyed God and was ashamed   7. Leah
____ Led tambourine dance of praise   8. Eve
____ Had two sons and died in child-   9. Tamar
   birth   10. Dinah
____ Made Moses keep Abraham's cove-
   nant sign
____ A slave whom God saved from death

Places. Write the number of EACH place before the phrase with which it is most closely associated.

____Noah stepped ashore
____"To your descendants I give
     this land."
____Destroyed because of their
     wickedness
____Covenant renewed with Jacob
____Home of Rebecca and Laban
____First sinners
____Sarah, Abraham, and Isaac
     buried
____City of Abraham's father

1. Sodom and
   Gomorrah
2. Ur
3. Eden
4. Bethel
5. Ararat
6. Hebron
7. Haran
8. Canaan

____Home of Jethro and
     Zipporah
____Jacob wrestled with God
____Jacob moved here from
     Haran
____Water blown aside for
     Israelites
____Piece of wood made water
     sweet
____Ten Commandments
____Food for complaining
     Israelites
____Hebrew slave labor built
     cities

1. Desert of Sin
2. Marah
3. Egypt
4. Peniel
5. Mt. Sinai
6. Shechem
7. Sea of Reeds
8. Midian

C. FEATURES

Background. Circle the letter of the ONE best answer.

1. Both tradition and most modern scholars agree that Genesis and Exodus were written by

   a. Moses
   b. a community of faith
   c. the same person or persons
   d. (an) anonymous writer(s)
   e. compilers of oral and written traditions

2. ALL of the following statements are true of Genesis EXCEPT:

   a. It contains both history and law.
   b. It tells Israel's story from creation to the death of Joseph.
   c. It reveals a special understanding of God, Israel, and history.
   d. It moves from east to west across the Fertile Crescent.
   e. It contains a strong pattern of persons.

3. Genesis means

   a. covering all time
   b. general history
   c. God's acts
   d. beginning
   e. b and c

4. Exodus means:

   a. arrival
   b. wandering
   c. the way out
   d. homecoming
   e. return

5. Exodus includes Israel's historical traditions from

   a. the call of Abraham to the covenant in Sinai
   b. slavery in Egypt to the covenant at Sinai
   c. the death of Joseph to entrance into the promised land
   d. creation to the death of Joseph
   e. departure from Egypt to the death of Moses

Special Themes and Content. Write either G for Genesis or E for Exodus in the blank before EACH item to show with which book it is most closely associated.

1. ____ Creation
2. ____ One long journey
3. ____ Disasters (Plagues)
4. ____ Fall of human race
5. ____ Twelve sons of Jacob
6. ____ Complaints
7. ____ Noah's ark
8. ____ Covenant Tent
9. ____ Ten Commandments
10. ____ Seven years of famine
11. ____ Covenant box
12. ____ "I will make you into a great nation."
13. ____ "Let my people go."
14. ____ Jealous brothers
15. ____ A family saga

Check answers on page 102. Compute your scores on page 104 and enter on the growth record for Unit 2 on page 106. Study any items you may have missed, looking up the Scripture references given. Then you will be ready to begin the study of Unit 3.

This map is for use with JUST FOR FUN on pages 57 and 58.

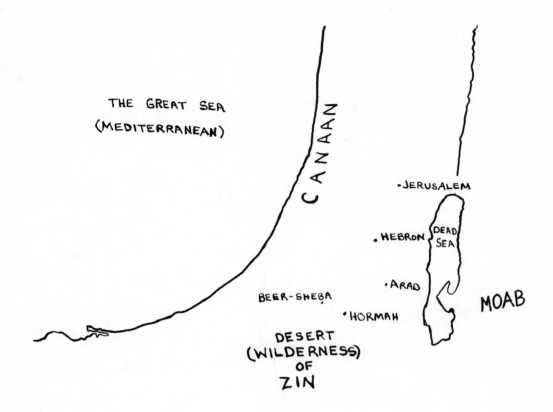

THE GREAT SEA
(MEDITERRANEAN)

CANAAN

·JERUSALEM

DEAD
SEA

·HEBRON

·ARAD

MOAB

BEER-SHEBA

·HORMAH

DESERT
(WILDERNESS)
OF
ZIN

·KADESH
(MERIBAH)

DESERT
(WILDERNESS)
OF
PARAN

·EZION-GEBER

GULF OF AQABA

HAZEROTH?·

? "GRAVES OF CRAVING"
· (KIBROTH-HATTA-AVAH)

·MT. SINAI?

UNIT 3: LEVITICUS, NUMBERS, AND DEUTERONOMY

OBJECTIVES

The same three categories are used in this unit as in Unit 2: Structure, Narrative, and Features. Upon completion of Unit 3, you will be able to do the following:

1. State the headings of the major divisions in Leviticus, Numbers, and Deuteronomy.
2. Number seven major events in order of their occurrence in these books.
3. Associate at least eight persons with events or descriptions in these books.
4. Associate at least seven places with events which happened there.
5. Identify at least five general conclusions of scholarship concerning the background of these books.
6. Distinguish among at least 20 special features as true of one of the three books.

In Unit 3, as in all units of this course, you are asked to take a pre-test in order to help you learn. If you score 90% or more, you may move directly to Book 2 of *Mastering Old Testament Facts*. However, most people will make very low scores on the pre-test because it measures knowledge of material yet to be learned. Don't let that bother you.

INSTRUCTIONS

Each page of guided reading in Unit 3 is divided by asterisks into three "frames."
DO NOT READ ALL THE WAY DOWN THE PAGE, but turn the page after reading a single frame.
You should proceed as follows:

1. Take the Unit 3 pre-test and record your score.
2. Study the introduction and outline as you begin each book.
3. Note the number and heading of each frame.
4. Read the Bible passages assigned. When asked to scan a passage, you may skip it, skim through it quickly, or read it. You will not be tested on it.
5. Try to answer the questions from memory. Just say the answers to yourself. You may write them if you wish, but it will double the time required.
7. When in doubt, look at the Bible to finish answering questions.
8. Then and ONLY THEN turn the page to check your answers. Exact wording does not usually matter.
9. Note the drawings to help remember the main points.

10. Do the Just-for-Funs if you find them fun; be sure to follow instructions given at the end of these frames.
11. Use section charts plus outlines to review the the structure and major themes of each book.
12. Take section tests as instructed, check answers and record your scores in the back of this book, then return to begin guided reading for the next biblical book.
13. Take the unit test. As you check answers, look up the references for any questions you miss.
14. Complete the Unit 3 Growth Record on page 106 and figure your growth in knowledge of the content of Leviticus, Numbers, and Deuteronomy.

Now begin the pre-test for Unit 3 on page 74.

PRE-TEST FOR UNIT 3

A. STRUCTURE

Circle the ONE BEST answer for each.

1. Leviticus can be divided into the following major subjects:

    a. Laws of sacrifice; Desert wanderings;
        Holiness Code; Moabite covenant
    b. Levites; Southern desert; Census; Deuter-
        onomic laws; Priestly laws
    c. At Sinai; Ordination of priests; Blessing
        and curse; Laws about holiness
    d. Laws of sacrifice; Ordination of priests;
        Clean and unclean; Day of Atonement;
        Laws about holiness
    e. Ten Commandments; Desert wanderings;
        Covenant ritual; Conclusion

2. Numbers can be divided into the following:

    a. At Sinai; In the southern desert; East
        of Jordan
    b. Ten Commandments; Desert wanderings;
        Joshua commissioned
    c. Confession of faith; Revolt of Israelites;
        Day of Atonement
    d. Census; First speech of Moses; Second
        speech of Moses; Conclusion
    e. Priestly law; Exhortation; Song of
        Moses; Conquering Canaan

3. Deuteronomy can be divided into the following:

    a. The Ten Commandments; First speech of
        Moses; Second speech of Moses; Cities
        of Refuge
    b. First speech of Moses; Second speech of
        Moses; Third speech of Moses; Conclusion
        to Pentateuch
    c. Miriam and Aaron rebel; Return of the
        spies; Worship of Baal, Death of Moses
    d. Census; Priestly law; Sacrifices;
        Conclusion to Pentateuch
    e. The twelve tribes; First Israelite wars;
        Exhortation; Confession of faith

Number the following events in the ORDER in which
they occur in Leviticus through Deuteronomy.

___Census is taken.

___Moses appoints Joshua.

___Miriam and Aaron criticize Moses.

___Strange fire kills Nadab.

___Balak asks Balaam to curse Israel.

___Poisonous snakes bite Israelites.

___Greedy people die eating quail.

B. NARRATIVE

Persons. Write the number of EACH of the following
persons before the ONE term most closely related
to it.

___Refused Balak's order   1. Miriam

___Wanted land east of Jordan   2. Aaron

___Turned leprous   3. Moses

___Reviewed Israelite history   4. Joshua

___He and descendants given priesthood   5. Balaam

___Only walking stick which bore fruit   6. Phineas

___Killed for rebelling against Moses   7. Korah

___A spy reports on Canaan   8. Tribe of
                                            Reuben

Places. Write the number of EACH of the following
places before the ONE term most closely associated
with it.

___Nazirite vow outlined   1. Sinai

___Southern desert   2. Kadesh

___Worship of Baal fought by Phinehas   3. Meribah

___Spies returned to report on Canaan   4. Paran

___Bronze serpent   5. Edom

___Covenant ritual   6. Peor

___Moses disobeyed God   7. Ebal

C. FEATURES

Background. Circle the letter of the ONE BEST
answer.

1. The most extensive block of priestly law in
    the Pentateuch is

    a. Leviticus 1--15
    b. Leviticus 1--27
    c. Leviticus 5--Numbers 16
    d. Exodus 28--Leviticus 27
    e. Exodus 25--Numbers 10

2. Numbers gets its name from

    a. The death of large numbers of Israelites
    b. A Hebrew word meaning desert, where most
        of the action takes place
    c. The first word in Numbers
    d. Chapters 1--4 which report a census
    e. Chapters 5--10 which contain numerous laws

3. Numbers resembles Exodus in ALL of the following ways EXCEPT:

   a. Contains chapters of priestly law
   b. Tells of the birth of Moses
   c. Is mainly geographic in organization
   d. Part tells of Israelites at Sinai
   e. Reports a miracle of feeding

4. Deuteronomy is mainly

   a. Reports of rebellion against Moses
   b. Priestly retellings of Passover and journey to Sinai
   c. Moses' discourses to the Israelites
   d. Stories of military conquests
   e. b and d

5. The setting of Deuteronomy is

   a. The desert at Mt. Sinai
   b. Canaan, the Promised Land
   c. Sinai, then Kadesh, then Moab
   d. Moab, east of the Jordan
   e. None of the above

Special content. Write ONE letter, L, N or D before EACH term to indicate that it is the most closely associated with Leviticus, Numbers, or Deuteronomy.

1. ___ Nazirite vow

2. ___ Law of Holiness

3. ___ Ten Commandments

4. ___ Moses' speeches

5. ___ Many revolts

6. ___ Love your neighbor as yourself

7. ___ Pigs and eels are unclean

8. ___ The donkey and the angel

9. ___ Deuteronomic Code

10. ___ Balaam blesses Israel

11. ___ Shema

12. ___ Aaron's walking stick blooms

13. ___ Offerings for Israel's sins

14. ___ Eight spies

15. ___ A scapegoat

16. ___ Confessions of faith

17. ___ Poisonous snakes

18. ___ The Lord bless you and take care of you

19. ___ Covenant ritual

20. ___ Covenant in Moab

Check answers on page 103. Compute your scores on page 104 and enter on the growth record for Unit 3, page 106.

OUTLINES

LEVITICUS

11	LAWS OF SACRIFICE	*(Chapters 1-7)*
12	ORDINATION OF PRIESTS	*(Chapters 8-10)*
13	CLEAN AND UNCLEAN	*(Chapters 11-15)*
14	DAY OF ATONEMENT	*(Chapter 16)*
15	LAWS ABOUT HOLINESS	*(Chapters 17-26)*
16	APPENDIX	*(Chapter 27)*

NUMBERS

21	AT SINAI	*(Chapters 1-10)*
22	IN THE SOUTHERN DESERT: PARAN	*(Chapters 10-20)*
23	EAST OF JORDAN: EDOM AND MOAB	*(Chapters 20-36)*

DEUTERONOMY

31	FIRST SPEECH OF MOSES	*(Chapters 1-4)*
32	SECOND SPEECH OF MOSES	*(Chapters 5-28)*
	32A Ten Commandments and Exhortation	
	32B Deuteronomic Laws	*(Chapters 12-26)*
	32C Conclusion: Blessing and Curse	
33	THIRD SPEECH OF MOSES	*(Chapters 29-30)*
34	CONCLUSION TO PENTATEUCH	*(Chapters 31-34)*

10 INTRODUCTION TO LEVITICUS

<u>Leviticus</u> takes it's name from the Levites, or tribe of Levi.
This tribe was responsible for religious ritual and instruction
in ancient Israel. The priesthood was a special group within it.

Leviticus consists almost entirely of ritual law or instruction
for the religious life of the people. It belongs to a great
block of Priestly Law, often called the Priestly Code, extending
from Exodus 25 to Numbers 10. Within Leviticus is found another
basic collection: the Laws about Holiness, or the Holiness Code
(ch. 17--26).

The whole of Leviticus is set at Sinai.

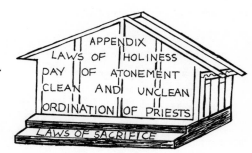

Turn to 10 on next page.

******************** ************

20 INTRODUCTION TO NUMBERS

The first four chapters of <u>Numbers</u> tell of a census, or numbering
of the people in the Sinai desert. The Hebrew name of this book,
"In the Desert," is far more appropriate for most of it's content;
for beginning at chapter 11 Numbers tells of Israel's adventures
and misadventures during the whole generation she spent in the
southern desert (Paran and Kadesh) and east of the Jordan (Moab).
The intervening chapters, 5--10, contain religious laws like
those in Leviticus.

Numbers is very closely related to Exodus 16--18, for both tell about incidents
that occurred in Israel's desert camps and travels. Also like Exodus, Numbers unfolds geographically:
At Sinai (ch. 1--10), in the southern desert (ch. 11--20), and east of Jordan (ch. 20--36).

Turn to 20 on next page.

****

30 INTRODUCTION TO DEUTERONOMY

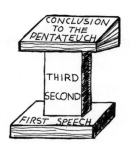

The name <u>Deuteronomy</u> means "second law" in Greek. It is so named
because the Ten Commandments of Exodus 20 are repeated, with
minor variations, in Deuteronomy 5, and because the whole book
represents a review of the Torah, or Law, found in Genesis--
Numbers.

The title of this book in Hebrew is Deuteronomy 1:1, <u>"These are the words</u> that Moses spoke to the people
of Israel when they were in the wilderness east of the Jordan River." This sentence accurately describes
the book, which consists of three discourses or speeches of Moses teaching Israel's faith and reviewing
God's good acts and demands. The long second speech of Moses incorporates yet another basic legal
collection: the Deuteronomic Laws of chapters 12--26, often called the Deuteronomic Code.
Deuteronomy is set in Moab at the end of Moses' life, just before Israel entered the Promised Land.

Turn to 30 on next page.

10 INTRODUCTION TO LEVITICUS

1. Leviticus gets it's name from _____.
2. Leviticus is part of the Priestly Law (or Code) which includes:

    a. Genesis 1--Deuteronomy 34

    b. Exodus 25--Numbers 10

    c. Leviticus 1--Numbers 10

    d. Leviticus 1--Deuteronomy 26

3. Leviticus is mostly

    a. Civil law

    b. Historical narrative

    c. Theological reflection

    d. Religious law

4. Leviticus includes a collection of laws called:

    a. Laws about Holiness

    b. The Ten Commandments

    c. The Book of the Covenant

    d. The Deuteronomic Code

5. The setting of Leviticus is:

    a. Jerusalem

    b. Moab

    c. Sinai

    d. Canaan

Check answers from information on previous page.

****

20 INTRODUCTION TO NUMBERS

1. Numbers gets it's name from _____.
2. The Hebrew name for Numbers means:

    a. "These are the names"

    b. "And God called"

    c. "In the desert"

    d. "These are the words"

3. Chapters 5--10 contain:

    a. Religious Laws

    b. Desert stories

    c. Prophetic oracles

    d. Census figures

4. Most of Numbers is about:

    a. The covenant at Sinai

    b. The wilderness years

    c. The covenant in Moab

    d. The duties of priests

5. The setting of Numbers is:

    a. Egypt/Sinai

    b. Sinai

    c. Sinai/Paran/Moab

    d. Moab

Check answers from information on previous page.

****

30 INTRODUCTION TO DEUTERONOMY

1. Deuteronomy gets its name from _____.
2. Deuteronomy consists of

    a. Speeches of Moses

    b. Teaching about Israel's faith

    c. Accounts of God's acts and demands

    d. All of the above

    e. None of the above

3. Deuteronomy includes a collection of laws called:

    a. The Priestly Code

    b. The Book of the Covenant

    c. The Holiness Code

    d. The Deuteronomic Code

4. The setting of Deuteronomy is:

_____

Check answers from information on previous page.

LEVITICUS

11 LAWS OF SACRIFICE (chapters 1--7)

Scan Leviticus 1--7.

Underscore names of sacrifices as you scan, and note the summary in
Leviticus 7:37-38.

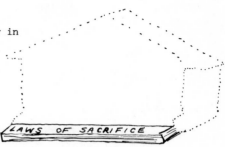

****

NUMBERS

21 AT SINAI (chapters 1--10)

Scan Numbers 1--10. (Stop at 10:10.)
Numbers 1--4 gives census results.
Read Numbers 6.

1. An Israelite who promised the Lord to refrain from wine, from
    cutting his hair and beard, and from touching any corpse, was
    said to have taken what vow?
2. Memorize the priestly blessing in Numbers 6:24-26.
    (Read verses 22-27.)

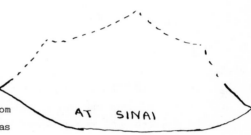

****

DEUTERONOMY

31 FIRST SPEECH OF MOSES (chapters 1--4)

Read Deuteronomy 1:1-18. Scan 1:9--3:29.
Read 4: 1-43.

1. Where did Moses deliver this historical review and
    exhortation to the Israelites?
2. How is his exhortation related to the historical review?

32   SECOND SPEECH OF MOSES (chapters 5--28)

32A Ten Commandments and Exhortation

Read Deuteronomy 4:44--6:25. Scan 7--11.

(Note: Here the Sabbath commemorates deliverance from slavery,
        not God's rest. See Ex. 20:11.)

Deuteronomy 6:4-5 is known as the "Shema"
from the Hebrew word "hear". Considered
the core of the law, what two main ideas
does it contain?

11

burnt (whole) offering   ordination offering

grain offering   fellowship offering

sin offering   repayment offering

(No need to memorize these).

******** *******************

21

1. The Nazirite vow
2. May the Lord bless you and take care of you;

    May the Lord be kind and gracious to you;

    May the Lord look on you with favor and give you peace.

Study the top portion of Section Chart 2 on page 92

then continue the guided reading on page 81.

Study the top portion of Section Chart 2 on page 92

then continue the guided reading on page 81.

****

31

1. In Moab, east of the Jordan River.
2. In exhorting them to obey God, Moses reminded them of the blessings which follow obedience and the calamities which follow disobedience, as in the past.

Study the top portion of Section Chart 3 on page 93. Then continue with 32A below.

Study the top portion of Section Chart 3 on page 93. Then continue with 32A below.

32A

One God only and complete love for him (Note sermon on this in chapters 6--11.)

12   ORDINATION OF PRIESTS (chapters 8--10)

Scan Leviticus 8--9.   Read Leviticus 10.

1.   Who are the priests? (Form a mental picture of the kinds of
things they do.)
2.   What reason does the writer give for the destruction of
Nadab and Abihu by strange fire?

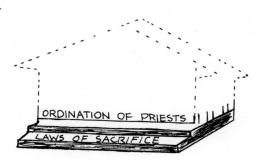

****

22   IN THE SOUTHERN DESERT: PARAN (chapters 10--20)

Read Numbers 10--14 (from 10:11).   Scan Numbers 15.

1.   Why was "Graves of Craving" (in Hebrew, "Kibroth-hattaavah")
so named?
2.   What happened to Miriam at Hazeroth? Why?
3.   The spies reported rich food in Canaan, but people like
giants. When ten spies urged returning to Egypt, what did
Caleb and Joshua say?
4.   The Israelites threatened to stone Caleb and Joshua. The
Lord then threatened to kill all the Israelites for rebelling.
When Moses begged mercy for the people, what was the Lord's
decision?

****

32B Deuteronomic Laws (chapters 12--26)
Read Deuteronomy 12.   Scan 13--17.   Read 18--19.

This collection of laws (12--26), often called the Deuteronomic
Code, applies to all of life.

1.   Forbidden an inheritance, what would the Levites receive?
2.   Why were six cities to be set apart?

12

1. Aaron and his sons
2. In the Sacred Tent they presented fire which the Lord had not
   commanded.

   Study the top portion of Section Chart 1 on page 91. Then
   continue guided reading on page 83.

```
****************************
```

22

1. Because the people craved meat, and when the Lord provided
   many quail, they died eating them
2. Miriam's skin was covered with a dreaded disease because
   she and Aaron criticized Moses for marrying a Cushite.
   (Note: Cush= Ethiopia)
3. That they must not rebel against the Lord, but should enter
   the land and God would give it to them
4. To let the people live, but not to allow that generation to
   enter Canaan

```
****************************
```

32B

1. The offerings: special parts of animals and first share of
   grain, wine, oil, and wool
2. So those who killed someone accidentally could find refuge

13 CLEAN AND UNCLEAN

Scan Leviticus 11--15.

Notice the kinds of creatures and kinds of conditions which are considered unclean. Also note the kinds of rules prescribed for dealing with uncleanness.

****

22   IN THE SOUTHERN DESERT   *(continued)*

Read Numbers 16--17.   Scan Numbers 18--19.
Read Numbers 20:1-13.

5.   What reason is given for the earthquake swallowing Korah and his followers?

6.   When the people blamed Moses and Aaron for the deaths of so many, the Lord commanded that the staffs of each tribal leader be placed in the tent. What was the result?

7.   At Meribah(="complaining") the Lord told Moses to speak to the rock and it would provide water. What wrong did Moses do that the Lord would not let him lead the people into Canaan?

****

32B Deuteronomic Laws *(continued)*

Scan Deuteronomy 20--23.   Read 24:1--26:15.

4.   Why were millstones not to be taken as security for a loan?

5.   Note that Deuteronomy 26:5-10a is a confession of faith, made when an Israelite offered his first fruits. "A wandering Aramean" refers to Jacob (Gen. 46). What great act of God does it proclaim?

13 Unclean creatures: (You need not memorize.)

     Animals which lack a divided hoof, chewing cud

     Water animals which lack scales and fins

     Winged insects which do not hop

     Some purification methods mentioned:

     Washing self, clothes, house, etc.

     Demolishing house

     Making offerings

****

22

5.   They revolted against Moses

6.   Aaron's walking stick blossomed and produced almonds.

7.   He failed to obey the Lord by speaking only. He hit the
       rock with his staff. (Note Ex. 17:1-7.)

REVOLT
AGAINST
MOSES

Study the middle portion of Section Chart 2 on page 92.
Then continue guided reading on page 85.

****

32B

4.   That would take away the family's means of living.

5.   God's deliverance of the Israelites from Egypt and his
      giving them Canaan

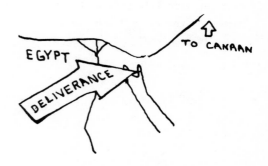

14 DAY OF ATONEMENT

Read Leviticus 16.

1. Why was the priest to go behind the curtain on the Day of Atonement?

2. What part were the two goats to have in Israel's purification from sin?

****

23 EAST OF JORDAN: EDOM AND MOAB (chapters 20--36)

Read Numbers 20--24. (Start at 20:14.)

1. When the Israelites complained again and were bitten by snakes, what did Moses do?

2. Why did Balaam beat the donkey he was riding?

3. When Balak, King of Moab, asked Balaam to curse Israel, what did Balaam do? Why?
    (Note that spoken words were thought to have power.)

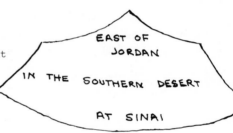

****

32C Conclusion: Blessing and Curse

Read Deuteronomy 26:16--27:14.   Scan 27:15--28:68.
Deuteronomy 26:16-19 is the contract the Israelites made with the Lord.

1. What did the Israelites promise the Lord?

2. Moses ordered a covenant ritual on Mounts Ebal and Gerizim. What were the Levites to pronounce while six tribes stood on Mt. Ebal?

3. Upon what did blessing or curse depend?

33 THIRD SPEECH OF MOSES

Scan Deuteronomy 29.   Read 30.

God commanded Moses to renew the covenant in Moab. In the Moabite Covenant, what choice must the Israelites make?

14

1. To purify Israel from sin.(Only this one day a year will he
   go behind the curtain.)
2. One is sacrificed to the Lord, and the other becomes a scapegoat
   (or goat "for Azazel") carrying all Israel's sins away.

****

23

1. He made a bronze snake, so that anyone who had been bitten
   could look at it and recover. (See John 3:14.)
2. Because the donkey balked when he saw an angel in front of him
3. Balaam blessed Israel three times because the Lord told him to
   bless. (He also prophesied the defeat of the Edomites and
   Moabites.)

JUST FOR FUN!   In chapters 21--24, identify two songs and five
                 oracles.

Answers: Songs--21:17-18, 27-30. Oracles--23:7-10, 18-24,
24:3-9, 15-19, 20-24.

****

32C

1. To have him for their God and to obey him.
2. Curses for disobeying the laws.
3. Obedience to God.

33

Life or death (blessing or curse)

Kinds of Uncleanness

The Laws of Purification (clean and unclean) were of such great influence on the life of Israel, that they caused dissension in the New Testament church. (See Acts 10 and 11.) Can you think of any counterparts in our history? (For example, bloodletting by leeches was once thought beneficial, until medical science learned that it was not.)

Can you identify five major kinds of uncleanness from these clues?

1. Legs, not roots   4. Reddish spot with hairs turned white

2. A baby's first cry   5. People cry and grieve.

3. Something oozes out

Answers: 1. Animals (11:1-47) 2. Childbirth 3. Bodily discharges 4. Dreaded skin disease 5. Contact with a corpse.

****** ***************** *****

JUST FOR FUN!   Where It Happened

You undoubtedly recognized these events as having occurred in Exodus where they were described in a slightly different way. You can compare them in Exodus 16 and 17. You can trace the Israelites route by finding the following places where these events occurred on the map, page 72. Then mark them on the map, page 94. As you label each place, recall an important event which happened there.

     "Graves of Craving" (Kibroth-hattavah)   Hormah

     Hazeroth   Meribah

     Kadesh

*************************＊**

JUST FOR FUN!   Jesus and Deuteronomy

Deuteronomy is the Old Testament book most often quoted in the New Testament. Why not check some of these more obvious references to Deuteronomy found in Matthew? (If you have a Bible with cross references, you may want to check other New Testament books for quotations and references to Deuteronomy.)

Matthew	Deuteronomy	Matthew	Deuteronomy
4:4	8:3	19:7	24:1-4
4:7	6:16	22:24	25:5
4:10	6:13	22:37	6:5
5:27	5:18	23:5	6:8
5:31	24:1	26:11	15:11
5:33	23:21	27:24	21:6-9
5:38	19:21	27:57-58	21:22-23

JUST FOR FUN!   Riddles

You may want to answer the last riddle after you have finished
studying Leviticus, as it refers to a passage not yet assigned.

1. How was Aaron like young Saul?

2. How were Eleazar and Ithamar like Solomon?

3. How were Aaron's granddaughters like the women of colonial
    New England?

Answers: 1) Lev. 8:12 2) Lev. 10:1-7;8:30; They remained faithful to God and their father when their
brothers disobeyed God and their father. Also they were anointed. 3) Lev.21:9.

*Study the middle portion of Section Chart 1, page 91.
Then continue guided reading on page 89.*

****

JUST FOR FUN!   Bronze Snake in the Desert

Think about the many complaints of the Israelites in the desert
and their many rebellions. The last one precedes the poisonous
snakes. With regard to the snakes:

1. What was different about the way the Lord relieved their
    suffering?

2. What significance do you see in this being the last reported
    complaint?

3. Do you see anything foreshadowed in the bronze snake?

Answers: 1) (Num. 21:9) The Israelites were healed only when they looked at the bronze snake.
For the first time help was not automatic, but required faith. 2) Participation of
the sufferer: increases motivation and awareness, and leads to growth. 3) Jesus on
the cross (John 3:14)

****

JUST FOR FUN!   Humanitarian Laws

The Deuteronomic Laws not only stress every aspect of an
individual's life, as areas for complete obedience to God, but they
also stress humanitarian concerns. They are, of course, most
appropriate for the culture of that day. Review the following
passages and consider why they were concerns in Old Testament
times, and where they are still concerns today. What is the
modern counterpart? What has been the shift of value emphasis
in the changes?

    Deuteronomy 15:1-18; 22:4,6-8; 22:5; 23:7-8; 24:5; 25:5-10

*Study the middle portion of Section Chart 3 on page 93.
Then continue guided reading on page 89.*

15 LAWS ABOUT HOLINESS (chapters 17--26)

Read Leviticus 17--19. Scan Leviticus 20--26.

1. What kinds of laws are included in the Holiness Code?
2. Why does the Lord say Israel should be holy?
3. Find a verse which Jesus quoted in his summary of the law.

16 APPENDIX

Scan Leviticus 27.

****

23 EAST OF JORDAN *(continued)*

Read Numbers 25.

4. How was Phinehas rewarded for stopping Baal worship?

Scan Numbers 26:1--27:11. Read Numbers 27:12-23.

5. Whom did the Lord order Moses to commission as leader in Moses' place?

Scan Numbers 28--30. Read Numbers 31--32.

6. After battling with the Midianites, what did the leaders of
    the tribes of Gad and Reuben request?

Scan Numbers 33--34. Read Numbers 35. Scan Numbers 36.

7. How many cities of refuge were to be built and where?

****

34 CONCLUSION TO THE PENTATEUCH (chapters 31--34)

Read Deuteronomy 31. Scan 32:1-44.
Read 32:45-52. Scan 33. Read 34.

1. What was Joshua commissioned to do?
2. Who was responsible for seeing that the people knew the law?
    (Note: Song of Moses is not the same as song at Reed Sea in
    Exodus 15.)
3. Why did Moses have to die on Mt. Nebo instead of entering Canaan?
4. After blessing the Israelites, Moses died and Joshua led the
    people. How had Joshua received the spirit of wisdom?

15

1. Dietary, marriage, and sexual laws, religious feasts, and
   Year of Restoration. Note: The collection of priestly laws in Leviticus
   17--26 is often called the Holiness Code. One of its characteristics
   is the refrain, "I am the Lord (your God)."
2. Be holy, because I, the Lord your God, am holy. (19:1-2)
3. Love your neighbor as you love yourself. (19:18)

*Study Section Chart 1, page 91, then take Section
Test 1 on page 95.*

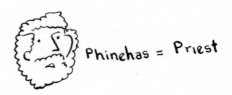

****

23

4. Phinehas and his descendants were permanently established
   as priests.
5. Joshua, son of Nun
6. Grazing land east of Jordan
7. Six, three on each side of the Jordan

*Study Section Chart 2, page 92, then take Section
Test 2 on page 96.*

****

34

1. To lead the Israelites into the Promised Land
2. The Levitical priests and the leaders of Israel
3. Because he dishonored God at Meribah
4. Moses appointed him by the laying on of hands.

*Study Section Chart 3, page 93, then take Section Test
3, page 97.*

SECTION CHART I: LEVITICUS

LAWS OF SACRIFICE
(chapters 1--7)

Offerings:

burnt   repayment
grain   ordination
sin   fellowship

ORDINATION OF PRIESTS
(chapters 8--10)

Aaron
and sons

Nadab and Abihu killed

for presenting illicit

fire

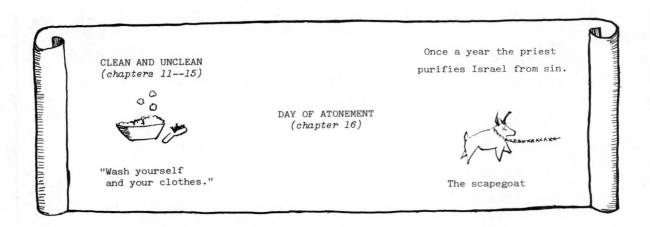

CLEAN AND UNCLEAN
(chapters 11--15)

"Wash yourself
and your clothes."

DAY OF ATONEMENT
(chapter 16)

Once a year the priest
purifies Israel from sin.

The scapegoat

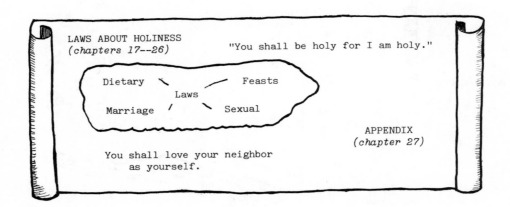

LAWS ABOUT HOLINESS
(chapters 17--26)   "You shall be holy for I am holy."

Dietary   Feasts
        Laws
Marriage   Sexual

APPENDIX
(chapter 27)

You shall love your neighbor
as yourself.

After studying the chart, take Section Test 1 on page 95.

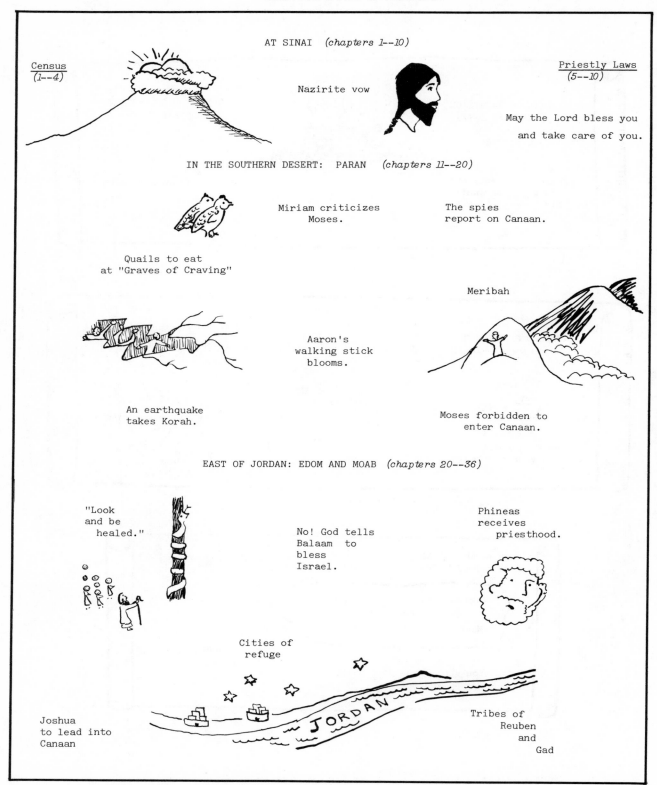

AT SINAI *(chapters 1--10)*

Census
(1--4)

Nazirite vow

Priestly Laws
(5--10)

May the Lord bless you
and take care of you.

IN THE SOUTHERN DESERT: PARAN *(chapters 11--20)*

Miriam criticizes
Moses.

The spies
report on Canaan.

Quails to eat
at "Graves of Craving"

Meribah

Aaron's
walking stick
blooms.

An earthquake
takes Korah.

Moses forbidden to
enter Canaan.

EAST OF JORDAN: EDOM AND MOAB *(chapters 20--36)*

"Look
and be
healed."

No! God tells
Balaam to
bless
Israel.

Phineas
receives
priesthood.

Cities of
refuge

JORDAN

Joshua
to lead into
Canaan

Tribes of
Reuben
and
Gad

After studying the chart, take Section Test 2 on page 96.

SECTION CHART 3: DEUTERONOMY

FIRST SPEECH OF MOSES

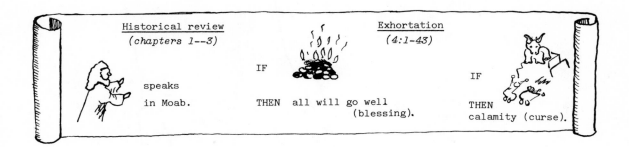

Historical review
(chapters 1--3)

speaks
in Moab.

IF

THEN   all will go well
(blessing).

Exhortation
(4:1-43)

IF

THEN
calamity (curse).

SECOND SPEECH OF MOSES

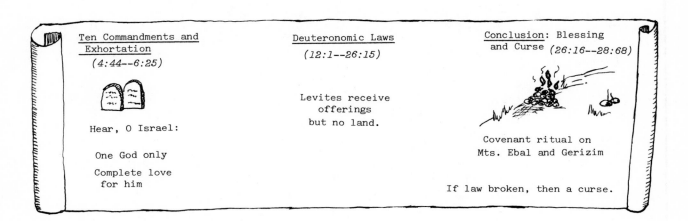

Ten Commandments and
Exhortation
(4:44--6:25)

Hear, O Israel:

One God only

Complete love
for him

Deuteronomic Laws
(12:1--26:15)

Levites receive
offerings
but no land.

Conclusion: Blessing
and Curse *(26:16--28:68)*

Covenant ritual on
Mts. Ebal and Gerizim

If law broken, then a curse.

THIRD SPEECH OF MOSES
(chapters 29--30)

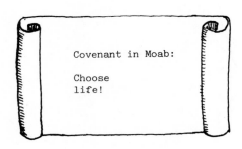

Covenant in Moab:

Choose
life!

CONCLUSION TO PENTATEUCH
(chapters 31--34)

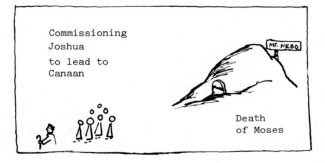

Commissioning
Joshua
to lead to
Canaan

Death
of Moses

After studying the chart, take Section Test 3 on page 97.

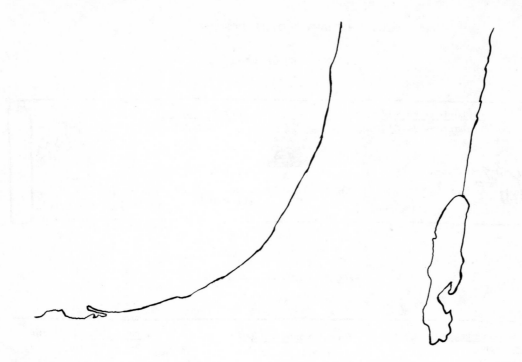

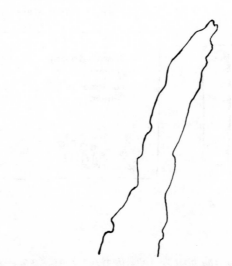

This map is for use with JUST FOR FUN on page 87.

SECTION TEST I: LEVITICUS

A. STRUCTURE

<u>Outline</u>. Complete the major headings of Leviticus.

   I. (1) Laws of _____

  II. (2) _____ of Priests

 III. (3) _____ and _____

  IV. (4) Day of _____

   V. (5) Laws about _____

  Appendix

B. FEATURES

<u>Background</u>. Circle the letter of the ONE BEST answer for each.

1. Priestly Law begins and ends as follows:

    a. Exodus 25--Leviticus 2
    b. Exodus 25--Numbers 10
    c. Leviticus 1--15
    d. Leviticus 1--27
    e. Leviticus 1--Numbers 10

2. One of the basic collections of law in the Pentateuch is:

    a. Laws of sacrifice
    b. Ordination of priests
    c. Laws of purification
    d. Laws about Holiness
    e. Law of Atonement

3. Priestly laws include ALL of the following EXCEPT:

    a. dietary laws
    b. royal laws
    c. marriage laws
    d. sexual laws
    e. religious feasts

4. All of Leviticus:

    a. consists of laws and rules
    b. is called Laws about Holiness
    c. tells of God's acts in history
    d. is the Decalogue
    e. applies to priests only

<u>Special content</u>. Check EACH item which refers to Leviticus.

1. __ Washing clothes after touching an animal which has died
2. __ Casting lots over goats
3. __ Sending two goats into the wilderness
4. __ Making a scapegoat out of one Israelite
5. __ Destroying Nadab by a strange fire
6. __ Purifying Israel from sins once a year
7. __ "You shall be my holy nation."
8. __ "Be holy because the Lord your God is holy."
9. __ "Love your neighbor as yourself."
10. __ The Ten Commandments are given.
11. __ Entering the Most Holy Place behind the curtain only once a year

Check answers on page 103. Compute your scores on page 104 and enter on the growth record for Unit 3, page 106. Review any items missed, then begin the study of Numbers on page 79.

SECTION TEST 2: NUMBERS

A. STRUCTURE

Outline. Complete the following outline of Numbers.

I. (1) _____

II. (2) _____

III. (3) _____

Sequence. Number the following events in the order in which they occur in Numbers.

___Joshua commissioned
___Revolt by Korah
___Cities of refuge planned
___Vow and priestly blessing
___Balaam's blessing
___Census
___Dreaded disease (leprosy)

B. NARRATIVE

Persons. Identify EACH of the following persons by writing the number of the name before the ONE term with which that person is most closely associated.

___Became covered with a dreaded
    disease
___King of Moab who wanted Israel
    cursed
___Received priesthood with his
    descendants
___Swallowed by an earthquake
___Almonds grew on his staff
___Defeated in battle
___Almost stoned for claiming
    Canaan
___Disobeyed God at Meribah
___Commissioned to lead Israelites
___Midianite prophet who obeyed
    the Lord

1. Moses
2. Aaron
3. Miriam
4. Joshua
5. Midianites
6. Phinehas
7. Balaam
8. Korah
9. Caleb
10. Balak

Places. Identify EACH place by writing the number before the ONE with which it is most closely associated.

___King wanted Israelites cursed
___In Paran where they waited
    for spies' return
___Tribes of Gad and Reuben found
    good grazing
___On both sides of Jordan
___Miriam and Aaron challenge
    Moses
___Nazirite vow outlined
___Israelites worshiped Baal
___Graves of craving
___Moses struck rock with staff
___Israelites were refused entry

1. Sinai
2. Kibroth-
    hattaavah
3. Hazeroth
4. Kadesh
5. Meribah
6. Peor
7. Eastern lands
8. Cities of
    Refuge
9. Edom
10. Moab

C. FEATURES

Background. Circle the letter of the ONE BEST answer for each.

1. Numbers received its name from

    a. The census reported in the first four
       chapters and chapter 26.
    b. The large number of enemies conquered
       in Canaan.
    c. The numbers given to the priestly laws.
    d. The large numbers of Israelites killed
       for disobedience.
    e. b and d

2. Numbers 5--10

    a. Contains a collection of laws on sacrifice.
    b. Tells of Moses' trials in getting the
       Israelites to leave Sinai.
    c. Describes the revolt led by Balak.
    d. Contains priestly laws begun in Exodus 25.
    e. b and c

3. The Hebrew name for Numbers

    a. Means "in the desert."
    b. Means "these are the names."
    c. Is highly misleading.
    d. Accurately describes its content.
    e. a and d

4. Numbers tells mainly about

    a. Receiving laws.
    b. Wandering in the wilderness.
    c. Conquering the promised land.
    d. The unfailing faith of the twelve tribes.
    e. a and c

Special content. Write an N for something associated with Numbers or an L for something associated with Leviticus.

___Letting hair grow
___Laws of Holiness
___Many revolts
___The Lord bless you
    and watch over you.
___Love your neighbor as
    yourself.
___Balaam's blessing
___Washing self after
    touching the dead
___Pigs and eels are
    unclean.
___An ass sees an angel.

___Expiating Israel's sins
___Aaron died.
___Israelites try to stone
    spies.
___Request for grazing land
___Scapegoat
___Poisonous snakes
___Joshua and Caleb only
    adults from Egypt to
    enter Canaan

Check answers on page 103. Compute your scores on page 104 and enter them on the growth record for Unit 3, page 106. Review any items missed, then begin the study of Deuteronomy on page 79.

A. STRUCTURE

Complete the following outline of Deuteronomy.

   I. (1) First Speech of _____

  II. (2) _____ of _____

       A. Ten Commandments and Exhortation
       B. (3) _____ Laws
       C. Conclusion: Blessing and Curse

 III. (4) _____ of _____

  IV. (5) _____ to the _____

B. NARRATIVE

Persons. Write the number of the ONE person most closely associated with EACH event on the blank
         before that event.

___Commissioned to lead into Canaan   1. Moses (Use twice)
___Forbidden to enter Canaan   2. Israelites
___To receive no inheritance of land   3. Levites
___Called to choose life   4. Joshua
___Blessed the twelve tribes

Places. Write the number of EACH place before the ONE term with which it is most closely associated.

___For accidental killers   1. Moab
___Promised Land   2. Canaan
___Moses died   3. Ebal and Gerizim
___Site of covenant ritual   4. Mt. Nebo
___Israelites heard Moses before entering Canaan   5. Six cities

C. FEATURES

Write the number of the ONE phrase most closely associated with EACH law or rite in the blank
before the law or rite.

___Shema (2 numbers)   1. Blessings always followed Israel's obedience
___Ten Commandments   2. Found in Exodus and Deuteronomy
___Confession of Faith   3. Choose life or death
___Israelite contract   4. Include all aspects of life
___Covenant ritual   5. Receiving spirit of wisdom
___Covenant in Moab   6. Hear, O Israel
___Historical review   7. Obedience to the Lord for national honor
___Laying on of hands   8. Laws on stone; curses by Levites
___Deuteronomic laws   9. Deliverance from Egyptian slavery
                     10. One God and complete love for him

*Check answers on page 103. Compute your scores on page 105 and enter them on the growth record for
Unit 3, page 106. After studying any items missed and reviewing the outlines and section charts,
take Unit Test 3 on next page.*

UNIT TEST 3: LEVITICUS, NUMBERS, AND DEUTERONOMY

A. STRUCTURE

Outline. Complete the following outlines.

   (1) Leviticus

      I. _____

     II. Ordination of Priests

   III. _____ and _____

    IV. Day of Atonement

     V. _____

   (2) Numbers

      I. _____

     II. _____

   III. _____

   (3) Deuteronomy

      I. _____

     II. _____

   III. _____

    IV. _____

Sequence. Number the following in the order in which they occurred in these books.

___Israel camps in southern desert (Paran).

___Moses dies.

___God decides rebels won't enter Canaan.

___Balak calls Balaam to curse Israel.

___Spies report on Canaan.

___God gives laws at Sinai.

___Israel renews covenant in Moab.

B. NARRATIVE

Persons. Identify EACH of the following persons by writing the number of the name before the ONE term with which it is most closely associated.

___Died from a strange fire.

___Almonds grew on his staff.

___Almost stoned for wanting to claim the Promised Land.

___Recited song at age 120.

___His donkey saw an angel.

___Became covered with a dreaded disease.

___Wanted land east of Jordan.

___Rebelled against Moses and Aaron.

1. Miriam
2. Caleb
3. Korah
4. Aaron
5. Moses
6. Balaam
7. Reuben and Gad tribes
8. Nadab and Abihu

Places. Write the number of EACH place before the ONE event with which it is most closely associated.

___The Lord sent quails.

___Moses disobeyed God.

___Spies reported on Canaan.

___Miriam and Aaron spoke against Moses.

___Choose life or death.

___Covenant ritual was carried out.

___Israelites worshiped Baal.

1. Ebal and Gerizim
2. Moab
3. "Graves of Craving"
4. Peor
5. Meribah
6. Hazeroth
7. Kadesh

C. FEATURES

Background. Circle the letter of the ONE BEST
answer for each question.

1. Priestly law is found

    a. Exodus 25--Leviticus 27
    b. Exodus 25--Numbers 10
    c. Leviticus 1--15
    d. Leviticus 1--27
    e. Leviticus 5--Numbers 16

2. Numbers is named from

    a. the numbers given to the priestly laws
    b. the census
    c. all the enemies conquered
    d. all the Israelites killed
    e. c and d

3. Numbers mainly describes

    a. laws on sacrifice
    b. Israelite wanderings
    c. fighting to conquer Canaan
    d. early legal matters
    e. growing faith of Israel

4. Deuteronomy is basically

    a. priestly law
    b. teaching Israel's faith
    c. God's good acts and demands
    d. prophecy
    e. b and c

5. Deuteronomy means

    a. second law
    b. covenant
    c. God's demands
    d. God's acts
    e. c and d

Special content. Write ONE letter, L, N, or D
before EACH term to indicate that the term is
most closely associated with Leviticus, Numbers,
or Deuteronomy.

1. ___Shema
2. ___Many revolts
3. ___Love your neighbor
4. ___Nazirite vow
5. ___The Lord bless you
6. ___Deuteronomic Laws
7. ___Wash after touching dead animals
8. ___Scapegoat
9. ___Balaam's blessing
10. ___Confession of faith
11. ___Laws of sacrifice
12. ___Pigs are unclean
13. ___Earthquake
14. ___Spies report
15. ___Laws of Holiness
16. ___Covenant in Moab
17. ___You shall be holy
18. ___Blessings and curses
19. ___A bronze serpent
20. ___Conclusion to Pentateuch

*Check answers on page 103 and compute your scores on page 105. Then enter your scores on the Unit
3 growth record on page 106. Determine your growth in knowledge by subtracting the % for pre-test
from the % score for the unit test. Refer to Scripture references for any answers you missed. Then
you will be ready to begin the study of Old Testament history in Book 2 of Mastering Old Testament Facts.*

PRE-TEST I *(50 points)*

A. CANON *(14)*

1. Canon	8. Pentateuch (or Law)
2. Jewish canon	9. Historical Books (or History)
3. Catholic canon	10. Poetry and Wisdom (or Poetry)
4. Protestant canon	11. Prophetic Writings(or Prophecy)
5. Law	12. b
6. Prophets	13. d
7. Writings	14. b

B. LITERATURE *(6)*

1. a; 2. a; 3. c; 4. d; 5. b; 6. d

C. HISTORY *(30)*

1. Israel, writings, canon

2.

Chronological order		Periods		Persons	
3	4	1. f	1. e	6. c	
7	9	2. b	2. f	7. j	
1	6	3. d	3. b	8. i	
10	5	4. a	4. d	9. g	
2	8	5. g	5. a	10. h	
		6. c			
		7. e			

SECTION TEST I *(20 points)*

1. d	11. b
2. c	12. e
3. c	13. d
4. b	14. List (or collection)
5. c	15. Sacred Scripture
6. d	16. Pentateuch
7. a	17. Historical Books
8. a	18. Poetry and Wisdom
9. c	19. Prophetic Writings
10. a	20. Apocryphal

SECTION TEST 2 *(15 points)*

Checks by 3, 5, 6, 8, 10

11. a
12. b
13. d
14. a
15. c

SECTION TEST 3 *(40 points)*

1. events
2. accounts (or books or stories), written
3. Sacred Scripture (or Scripture)

Events *(20)*	Date
1. Call of Abraham	c.1950–c.1550 B.C.
2. Exodus	c.1250 B.C.
3. David takes Jerusalem	c.1000 B.C.
4. Fall of Samaria	721 B.C.
5. Josiah's reform	621 B.C.
6. Fall of Jerusalem	587 B.C.
7. Edict of Cyrus	538 B.C.
8. Zerubbabel's Temple	515 B.C.
9. Alexander the Great	333 B.C.
10. Maccabean revolt	165 B.C.

Section Test 3 *(continued)*

Persons *(10)*				Periods
Chronological order:		Matching:		(Any order will do)
4	1 5	1. d		1. Ancestors
3	2	2. b		2. Egypt
		3. a		3. Judges
		4. e		4. Monarchy
		5. c		5. Exile
				6. Persian period
				7. Greek period

UNIT TEST I *(50 points)*

A. CANON *(12)*

1. A list of writings accepted as Sacred Scripture by Jews and Christians. (Any wording of the same idea is satisfactory.)
2. Jewish, Catholic, Protestant
3. Law, Prophets, Writings
4. Pentateuch, Poetry and Wisdom, Historical Books, Prophetic Writings
5. Deuterocanonical, Apocryphal
6. Thirty-nine (39)

Identifying canons:

1. J	4. J	*If you made errors,*
2. P	5. C and P	*review pages 7-12.*
3. C	6. P	

B. LITERATURE *(8)*

1. Any three of the following:

Victory song	Annal
Oracle	Court history
Thanksgiving song	Letter
Elegy (or Funeral song)	Myth
Fable	Legend
Riddle	Saga

2. Canonical category	3. b	*Review material on*
Literary type	4. d	*pages 14-15.*
	5. a	
	6. c	

7-8. Any two of these ideas:
   --Finest literature of ancient Israel
   --Includes masterpieces of Hebrew language and culture
   --Literary treasure of the human race
   --Has shaped and nourished English Language (through King James Version)
   --Portions memorized by millions of people

C. HISTORY *(30)*

1. Israel; 2. The writings (or literature); 3. The canon

Chronological order:		Match events with dates:		Match persons with events:	
3 4 2 5		1. e	6. b	1. c	6. i
1 7 6		2. a	7. g	2. j	7. h
		3. h	8. d	3. e	8. d
		4. f	9. i	4. g	9. f
		5. j	10. c	5. a	10. b

Errors? Review pages 17-24.

ANSWERS FOR UNIT 2

PRE-TEST 2 (100 points)

A. STRUCTURE (30)

Outlines (8)

1. b	5. c
2. e	6. e
3. a	7. a
4. a	8. b

Sequence (22)

I.	II.	III.	IV.
1	4	5	4
6	6	3	3
2	1	4	2
4	5	2	5
5	2	1	1
3	3		

B. NARRATIVE (50)

Relationships (10)

PC	PC	PC
S	B	HW
PC	B	SB
		HW

Women (10)

4	6
7	5
2	3
8	10
1	9

Men (15)

3	4	2
5	2	4
1	5	5
2	1	1
4	3	3

Places (15)

5	3
8	5
4	7
7	1
2	6
1	4
6	2
3	

C. FEATURES (20)

Background (5)

1. d
2. a
3. e
4. e
5. c

Special Content (15)

G	G	E
G	E	G
E	E	E
E	G	G
E	E	G

SECTION TEST I (50 points)

A. STRUCTURE (15)

Outline (9)

	Sequence (6)
1. THE BEGINNINGS OF HUMANITY	2
2. Creation of the Universe	6
3. Disobedience and Disorder	4
4. The Flood and the Tower of Babylon	1
5. THE BEGINNINGS OF ISRAEL	3
6. TO CANAAN: ABRAHAM, SARAH, AND ISAAC	5
7. The Call to Leave Home	
8. The Covenant with Abraham	
9. Isaac, the Promised Son	

B. NARRATIVE (35)

Happenings (4) — **Places (10)** — **Relationships (7)**

Happenings	Places		Relationships
1. d	4	2	Adam
2. a	8	7	Abraham
3. e	6	1	Abraham
4. b	3	5	Isaac
	9	10	Seth
			Isaac
			Ishmael

Women (5) — **Men (9)**

Women	Men	
2	5	9
3	6	2
2	1	7
1	8	4
4	3	

SECTION TEST 2 (50 points)

A. STRUCTURE (15)

Outline (10)

	Sequence (5)
1. IN CANAAN AND HARAN: JACOB	4
2. Forced to Leave Canaan	2
3. Riches and Troubles in Haran	5
4. The Return to Canaan	1
5. THE MOVE TO EGYPT: JOSEPH, THEN ISRAEL	3
6. Dreams and Misfortunes	
7. Joseph's Rise to Power	
8. Reunion with Brothers	
9. Israel's Move to Egypt	
10. Deaths of Jacob and Joseph	

B. NARRATIVE (35)

Happenings (5) — **Places (8)**

Happenings	Places	
1. c	5	1
2. e	3	4
3. d	6	2
4. e	8	7
5. d		

Relationships (8) — **Women (5)** — **Men (9)**

Relationships		Women	Men	
Isaac	Jacob	3	4	8
Jacob	Joseph	5	9	2
Jacob	Judah	2	7	6
Judah	Perez	1	3	5
		4	1	

SECTION TEST 3 (33 points)

A. STRUCTURE (10)

Outline (4)

	Sequence (6)
1. EGYPT: MOSES AND THE EXODUS	3
2. Oppression: Call of Moses	6
3. Disasters (Plagues)	2
4. Deliverance: Passover and Exodus	5
	1
	4

B. NARRATIVE (23)

Happenings (5) — **Persons (8)** — **Places (10)**

Happenings	Persons		Places	
1. b	4	8	5	2
2. e	7	3	1	3 & 1
3. a	1	5	6	5 & 4
4. d	6	2	1	6
5. e			4	4

A. STRUCTURE *(15)*

Outline *(4)*   Sequence *(11)*

1. DESERT: JOURNEY TO SINAI   5   2
2. AT SINAI   3   9
3. Covenant and Law   6   7
4. Priestly Laws: The Sacred Tent   4   10
                                     1   8
                                    11

B. NARRATIVE *(18)*

Happenings *(5)*   Persons *(6)*   Places *(7)*

  1. b   4   5   5   1
  2. c   3   2   1   2
  3. d   1   1   4   3
  4. a   6
  5. e

UNIT TEST 2 *(100 points)*

A. STRUCTURE *(30)*

Outline *(15)*

Genesis:

1. THE BEGINNINGS OF HUMANITY
2. Creation of the Universe
3. Disobedience and Disorder
4. The Flood and the Tower of Babylon
5. THE BEGINNINGS OF ISRAEL
6. TO CANAAN: ABRAHAM, SARAH, AND ISAAC
7. IN CANAAN AND HARAN: JACOB
8. THE MOVE TO EGYPT: JOSEPH, THEN ISRAEL

Exodus:

1. EGYPT: MOSES AND THE EXODUS
2. Oppression: Call of Moses (Disasters-plagues)
3. Deliverance: Passover and Exodus
4. DESERT: JOURNEY TO SINAI
5. AT SINAI
6. Covenant and Law
7. Priestly Laws: the Sacred Tent

(For review, see outlines, page 38, and section charts, pages 59-62.)

Sequence *(15)*

I.   3 (Gn.21)   II. 2 (Gn.41)   III. 2 (Ex.16)
     5 (Gn.32)   5 (Ex.12)   4 (Ex.24)
     1 (Gn.4)   4 (Ex.4)   5 (Ex.32)
     4 (Gn.24)   1 (Gn.37)   3 (Ex.20)
     2 (Gn.9)   3 (Ex.2)   1 (Ex.14)

Unit Test 2 *(continued)*

B. NARRATIVE *(50)*

Relationships *(8)*   Men *(16)*

1. Adam, Seth (Gn.4--5)   5 (Gn.19)   8 (Ex.4)
2. Abraham, Isaac (Gn.21)   4 (Gn.12)   3 (Gn.29)
3. Abraham, Ishmael (Gn.16) 8 (Gn.22)   5 (Gn.41)
4. Isaac, Jacob (Gn.25)   1 (Gn.3)   2 (Gn.32)
5. Jacob, Joseph (Gn.30)   3 (Gn.9)   7 (Ex.18)
6. Jacob, Judah (Gn.29)   7 (Gn.20)   4 (Gn.44)
7. Judah, Perez (Gn.38)   6 (Gn.14)   6 (Ex.4)
8. Moses (Ex.2)   2 (Gn.4)   1 (Ex.33)

   Women *(10)*   Places *(16)*

  7 (Gn.29)   5 (Gn.8)   8 (Ex.2)
  9 (Gn.38)   8 (Gn.17)   4 (Gn.32)
  5 (Gn.17)   1 (Gn.19)   6 (Gn.33)
 10 (Gn.30)   4 (Gn.28)   7 (Ex.14)
  2 (Gn.27)   7 (Gn.29)   2 (Ex.15)
  8 (Gn.3)   3 (Gn.2)   5 (Ex.20)
  1 (Ex.15)   6 (Gn.23,   1 (Ex.16)
  4 (Gn.35)   25,35)   3 (Ex.1)
  6 (Ex.4)   2 (Gn.11)
  3 (Gn.21)

C. FEATURES *(20)*

Background *(5)*

1. c
2. a
3. d
4. c
5. b   *(See page 39)*

Special Themes and Content *(15)*

1. G (1--2)   9. E (20)
2. E (14--19)   10. G (41)
3. E (7--10)   11. E (25,37)
4. G (3)   12. G (12)
5. G (49)   13. E (5--10)
6. E (16--17)   14. G (37)
7. G (6--9)   15. G (12--50)
8. E (26,36)

ANSWERS FOR UNIT 3

PRE-TEST 3 *(50 points)*

A. STRUCTURE *(10)*   **B. NARRATIVE** *(15)*

1. d	2
2. a	7
3. b	4
	1
	6
	5
	3

Persons *(8)*	Places *(7)*
5	1
8	4
1	6
3	2
6	5
2	7
7	3
4	

C. FEATURES *(25)*

Background *(5)*   Special Content *(20)*

1. e	1. N	8. N	15. L	
2. d	2. L	9. D	16. D	
3. b	3. D	10. N	17. N	
4. c	4. D	11. D	18. N	
5. d	5. N	12. N	19. D	
	6. L	13. L	20. D	
	7. L	14. N		

SECTION TEST 1 – LEVITICUS *(20 points)*

A. STRUCTURE *(5)*   **B. FEATURES** *(15)*

1. Laws of sacrifice	1. b 1
2. Ordination of priests	2. d 2
3. Clean and unclean	3. b 5
4. Day of Atonement	4. a 6
5. Laws about Holiness	8
	9
	11

SECTION TEST 2 – NUMBERS *(50 points)*

A. STRUCTURE *(10)*

Outline	Sequence
1. At Sinai	6 5
2. In the Southern Desert:	4 1
Paran	7 3
3. East of Jordan: Edom	2
and Moab	

B. NARRATIVE *(20)*   **C. FEATURES** *(20)*

Persons		Places		Background	Special Content	
3	5	10	1	1. a	N	N
10	9	4	6	2. d	L	L
6	1	7	2	3. a	N	N
8	4	8	5	4. b	N	N
2	7	3	9		L	N
					N	L
					L	N
					L	N

SECTION TEST 3 – DEUTERONOMY *(25 points)*

A. STRUCTURE *(5)*

1. First Speech of Moses
2. Second Speech of Moses
3. Deuteronomic Laws
4. Third Speech of Moses
5. Conclusion to the Pentateuch

SECTION TEST 3 *(continued)*

B. NARRATIVE *(10)*   **C. FEATURES** *(10)*

Persons	Places	
4	5	6, 10 3
1	2	2 1
3	4	9 5
2	3	7 4
1	1	8

UNIT TEST 3 *(50 points)*

A. STRUCTURE *(10)*

Outlines *(3)*   Sequence *(7)*

1. Leviticus:
   Laws of Sacrifice
   Clean and Unclean
   Laws about Holiness
2. Numbers:
   At Sinai
   In the Southern Desert
   East of the Jordan
3. Deuteronomy:
   First Speech of Moses
   Second Speech of Moses
   Third Speech of Moses
   Conclusion to the Pentateuch

Sequence *(7)*
2 (Num. 10)
7 (Deut. 34)
4 (Num. 14)
5 (Num. 22)
3 (Num. 13)
1 (Lev. 1-- Num. 10)
6 (Deut. 29)

(For review, see outlines, page 76 and section charts, pages 91 - 93.)

B. NARRATIVE *(15)*

Persons *(8)*	Places *(7)*
8 (Lev. 10)	3 (Num. 11)
4 (Num. 17)	5 (Num. 20)
2 (Num. 14)	7 (Num. 13)
5 (Deut. 32, 34)	6 (Num. 12)
6 (Num. 22)	2 (Deut. 30)
1 (Num. 12)	1 (Deut. 27)
7 (Num. 32)	4 (Num. 25, Deut. 4)
3 (Num. 16)	

C. FEATURES *(25)*

Background *(See Introduction, p. 77.)*
1. b *(5)*
2. b
3. b
4. e
5. a

Special Content *(20)*

1. D (6)	11. L (1--10)
2. N (10--25)	12. L (11)
3. L (19)	13. N (16)
4. N (6)	14. N (13)
5. N (6)	15. L (17-26)
6. D (12--26)	16. D (29)
7. L (11)	17. L (19)
8. L (16)	18. D (27-28)
9. N (23--24)	19. L (21)
10. D (26)	20. D (31--34)

(Chapter numbers for review are given in parenthesis.)

After checking answers for a test, record the number correct for each category in the blanks in the # column. (To find % score for each category follow directions, using % charts found on the next page or multiplying.) Then add the number correct in the categories to find the total correct for the test and follow directions for the % score. Record the test score here and on the growth record, page 106.

UNIT 1

Pre-test for Unit 1

Category	# Correct		% Score	Directions
A. Canon	_____	=	_____	See % chart for 14.
B. Literature	_____	=	_____	See % chart for 6.
C. History	_____	=	_____	See % chart for 30.
Total (A+B+C)	_____ x2=	_____ %		

Section Test 1

% = # correct x 5

Section Test 2

% = # correct x 20 ÷ 3

Section Test 3

% = # correct x 5 ÷ 2

Unit Test 1

Category	# Correct		% Score	Directions
A. Canon	_____	=	_____	See % chart for 12.
B. Literature	_____	=	_____	See % chart for 8.
C. History	_____	=	_____	See % chart for 30.
Total (A+B+C)	_____ x2=	_____ %		

UNIT 2

Pretest for Unit 2

Category	# Correct		% Score	Directions
A. Structure	_____	=	_____	See % chart for 30.
B. Narrative	_____	=	_____	# times 2
C. Features	_____	=	_____	# times 5
Total (A+B+C)	_____	=	_____	# = %

Section Test 1

Category	#Correct		% Score	Directions
A. Structure	_____	=	_____	See % chart for 15.
B. Narrative	_____	=	_____	See % chart for 35.
C. Total (A+B)	_____ x2=	_____ %		

Section Test 2

Category	#Correct		% Score	Directions
A. Structure	_____	=	_____	See % chart for 15.
B. Narrative	_____	=	_____	See % chart for 35.
C. Total (A+B)	_____ x2=	_____ %		

UNIT 2 (continued)

Section Test 3

Category	#Correct		% Score	Directions
A. Structure	_____	=	_____	# correct x 10
B. Narrative	_____	=	_____	See % chart for 23.
Total (A+B)	_____	=	_____ %	Multiply by 3, then add 1.

Section Test 4

Category	# Correct		% Score	Directions
A. Structure	_____	=	_____	See % chart for 15.
B. Narrative	_____	=	_____	See % chart for 18.
Total (A+B)	_____	=	_____	Multiply by 3, then add 1.

Unit Test 2

Category	# Correct		% Score	Directions
A. Structure	_____	=	_____	See % chart for 30.
B. Narrative	_____	=	_____	# correct x 2
C. Features	_____	=	_____	# correct x 5
Total (A+B+C)	_____	=	_____	# = %

UNIT 3

Pre-test for Unit 3

Category	# Correct		% Score	Directions
A. Structure	_____	=	_____	# correct x 10
B. Narrative	_____	=	_____	See % chart for 15.
C. Features	_____	=	_____	# correct x 4
Total (A+B+C)	_____ x2=	_____ %		

Section Test 1

Category	#Correct		% Score	Directions
A. Structure	_____	=	_____	# x 20 = %
B. Features	_____	=	_____	See % chart for 15.
Total (A+B)	_____ x5=	_____ %		

Section Test 2

Category	#Correct		% Score	Directions
A. Structure	_____	=	_____	# correct x 10
B. Narrative	_____	=	_____	# correct x 5
C. Features	_____	=	_____	# correct x 5
Total (A+B+C)	_____ x2=	_____ %		